Mourning Became Mrs. Spendlove

AND OTHER PORTRAITS, GRAVE AND GAY

Mourning

BECAME MRS. SPENDLOVE

and other Portraits, Grave and Gay

BY OLIVER ST. JOHN GOGARTY

CREATIVE AGE PRESS · NEW YORK

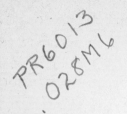

Contents

24 Sept. 1936

5-00

Mourning Became Mrs. Spendlove

Have YOU EVER EXPERIENCED the annoyance that obsesses you when you come across a name that seems familiar and full of associations and which, nevertheless, you cannot place? Last night I had just such a tantalizing experience. I was turning over the pages of *The Principal Voyages of the English Nation* by Richard Hakluyt, when I came across: "The names of all the men, women, and children which arrived safely in Virginia and remained to inhabit there, 1587." There they were, all the brave and simple names of England, names of one syllable for the humbler folk: Pratt, Howe, Dare, Cage; then names of two syllables for that solid body of the middle class from which all the greatness of the nation proceeds: Newton, Stillman, Chapman; and next there were names of three syllables for those who probably turned out to be leaders or wastrels (sometimes there is little difference): Merrimoth, Hemmington, Mannering.

Drawn by some strange attraction I looked again, and my eye fell upon the name of "Spendlove," "John Spendlove." Where had I heard that name? With what was it associated? There was some mixture of mirth and tragedy in it that I could not recall. I resolved not to force my memory so hard that it would lose the elasticity by which, if left alone, it recovers itself. Desultorily I read on, and gradually memory began to revive and to recover a long-lost story. It was the name "John" that retarded it. "Spendlove" in my story belonged to a woman, and "John" was the name of one of Scotland Yard's Big Four who recounted the tale to me.

It was in the reign of good Queen Victoria, the days of the side whiskers, the skirted frock coat, the hansom cab, the irreproachable family life, and—alas—St. John's Wood. Every married man modelled himself on that paragon of husbands, the Prince Consort. If there were any other consort in the life of a model Englishman, she was sure to be concealed, with all the secrecy due to respectability, in some shady and comfortable villa, tree embowered, and set back from the road. Some of the villas were approached by a little drive or avenue. It was all so comely, respectable, and unobtrusive. Anything can be tolerated in English life so long as it remains unobtrusive. Even a foible is forgiven so long as it ruffles not the calm tenor of respectability.

Gentle Reader, if you take exception to my employment of the word "respectable" in the list of adjectives by which I am striving to reproduce the atmosphere in which Jemima Spendlove lived when she was in her twenties and as lovely and as illiterate as Lady Hamilton, indulge me. St. John's Wood may justify itself.

The big man from Scotland Yard told me all. He did

not tell it as I must tell it, because all he had to go on was an official report. "We had to look up her antecedents," he explained. Now what can be more unfair to one whose antecedents are being looked up than an official report? An official report can be the worst of all prejudiced construings because it is shorn of all pathos, sympathy, understanding, and romance—of everything human, in fine. It lacks imagination. It lacks humor, and, the greatest deprivation of all, it lacks a background. There was no background in the official report, no Windsor tapestry behind Jemima Spendlove. In the end she was constrained to supply it for herself. In her attempt to make up for this deficit lay tragedy. This I attribute to the shortcomings of the official report.

According to this, she came from a village in Shropshire (a dangerous place for lassies if the "lads" are in love). Her brother was a second footman in a house in Grosvenor Square. He deposed that he had lost touch with his sister. Her parents had lost touch with her, but they did not regard it as a calamity that they did not know her address. If Jemima had not the usual background of young women in her position—"my father's rectory"—at least her parents were parishioners. They were of that fiber that makes for righteousness and integrity, backbones of the country. In fact, they found themselves in similar circumstances to those parents who hymned:

> We drinks the champagne wot she sends us;
> But we NEVER will forgive.

The report went on to say that Jemima packed a suitcase, on the tenth of a certain August, for a sporting guest who, before starting out for Scotland and the Glorious Twelfth, was having a shakedown in the closed townhouse of a friend where Jemima was employed. Coincidentally with his return from Scotland, Jemima disappeared into "The Wood."

It must not be forgotten, if we are to restore Jemima's background, that there lived in the decorous days of the good Queen, Her Majesty's Poet Laureate who, in that long peace, had leisure to take uninterrupted flights into regions of imagination and romance. And what could be more imaginative and romantic than the legends of King Arthur—that almost virginal prototype of the almost virginal Prince Consort himself? Strictly, here the comparison must stop. So Alfred wrote the *Idylls of the King*, which consisted of little vignettes of the Queen's dalliance with Sir Lancelot. (What better lot could a knight have than to be called by a name with a lance in it? The aptness of those English names again!) These tales in delectable blank verse of languishing maidens of impeccable virtue and brave knights had the effect of casting a glamor over the affairs of merchant princes, gentlemen of private means, and certain gilded guardsmen. They had the effect of turning St. John's Wood into a Camelot, and every little villa in it into that room in Shallot where not reality, but its reflection, was surveyed through a magic mirror. Owing to the enchantment cast over the reign by the Laureate, adultery became not only respectable but almost edifying—with the reservation of the righteous parents of Jemima mentioned above. The faultless poet became a peer, a thing almost as unprecedented as a peer becoming a poet; but we must remember that the poet addressed a select, appreciative, and grateful audience.

For ten years Jemima lived in that secular seclusion which only London can assure, a town where everyone minds his own business—which goes to show that there is something to be said for "a nation of shopkeepers" after all. Were it not for her address—and your address is half your reputation in London—her reputation might have been irreproachable as that of the wife of some admiral absent on empire-building, or as that of some bearer of the White Man's Burden thinking imperially through the watches of a tropic night, with a tropical charmer reclining on either shoulder. But St. John's Wood—even the most philanthropic ladies of Berkely Square never mentioned it!

For ten years, then, Jemima's Lancelot was constantly in attendance. He visited the villa once a week; and, if the times of his visits were not predictable, his confidence was all the more to the credit of Jemima whose "honor, rooted in dishonor, stood."

One Friday in the autumn of the eleventh year, instead of the anonymous letter with the bank notes, Jemima received a large check and the information that it was sent at the express wish of one of the signatory's clients, who was left unnamed. It was signed on behalf of the most reputable (because of their skill in disposing of the disreputable) firm of Robb, Robb, Crooks, & Swannell.

Jemima became cold at first when she realized the letter's import. Then she was filled with consternation. She gasped and fell back in one of the hall chairs in which no one had ever sat before.

Perceiving the untoward lull after the hall door had been opened, Mrs. Shabedge, the cook, who had been acting as lady-in-waiting at the head of the kitchen stairs, came into the open. She saw the pale face of Jemima. She suspected the worst: "So poor Mr. Darige is dead!" Then she thought of something worse still: "That's the way they behave when they're going to get married."

Jemima recovered consciousness. She burst into tears. He was lost to her either way. And her tears were genuine, for what woman, outside Turkey of the old regime, can be faithful to a man without forming a habit and permitting intimacy to turn into affection? Dead or wed he would visit her no more.

Florrie, who acted as lady's maid, parlor maid, companion, and, of an evening, fortune teller—for those who have no future take most trouble to have it foretold—and Florrie could tell your fortune by the pattern that the tea leaves left when you turned down your empty cup—happened to arrive at this moment from an errand for the cook. She learned the sad news with dismay. What was to be done? Write to the Firm, was the suggestion of Mrs. Shabedge. But Florrie, who lived more in the present, said that the first thing to be done was to go out and buy yourself some decent mourning before the emporiums would be closed. This was obvious. The cook concurred.

"I have never worn mourning in my life," Jemima objected.

"Well, I have," Mrs. Shabedge said, "and I wish to

God I wuz wearin' it again. Wait a minit till I put on my cape."

The foreman of the furnishings store was a typical English salesman. One of those who would put a go-getting, assaulting, American salesman in the shade. Instead of thrusting his wares on you, he took you into partnership with himself, as it were, while conceding to you the privilege of benefitting by his taste which bore a close affinity to cost. He received the whispered confidence of the cook coldly. He addressed himself to Madame. "A young widow cannot express too much grief by her raiment; but we must temper it with taste." The question arose about a bonnet. "There's more in a bonnet than you could ever tell. Before choosing, I would like you to consult Miss Thorpe. Will you ask Miss Thorpe to step this way?" he said to an eavesdropping saleswoman.

Miss Thorpe appeared breastless. In some mysterious way, this peculiarity of her figure suggested bereavement. It seemed as if it were her contribution to the general loss. She balanced a widow's poke on her hand which she held splayed inside the bonnet. With her free hand she adjusted the ribands and turned the thing in every direction, but with a motion far removed from sprightliness: there was inexpressible sadness in the movements of the imaginary head, a sadness which appealed greatly to Jemima. She was all out for making a purchase at once. With native foresight, Mr. Tompkins asked would Madame be kind enough to inspect his stock? There were other very becoming shapes.

Mrs. Shabedge opined, "It's a bit too smart and purty. Where does the 'art-break come in?""

Icily Miss Thorpe said, "They are worn like this nowadays."

There remained only Florrie to satisfy. Jemima's mind was made up.

Florrie had a suggestion to make, "What abart a bit o' white crinkle-like around the rim?""

"When one is entering second mourning a little relief will be permissible; but not till then," said Miss Thorpe.

Perhaps it was to give trouble and so "get her own back" that Mrs. Shabedge suggested that Jemima put them on now. "We don't want to be seen goin' about too bright after a death in the 'ouse so to speak."

"This way," said Mr. Tompkins, leaving the ladies to Miss Thorpe.

Later, when leaving the emporium, Jemima extended her hand to Mr. Tompkins. That experienced salesman put his behind his back as if the gesture were a part of the bow he was making. He bowed as one unworthy of the privilege or familiarity or whatever it was. Subsequently he remarked in explanation to Miss Thorpe that it didn't do to make free with customers. They must be kept in their place. Miss Thorpe agreed. She did not think . . . if you asked her, she would not say that there was much class to them anyway: no relatives, and making free with her maid, and putting up with that vulgar fat woman.

But the effect on Jemima was profound. She attributed the deferential, nay, subservient manner of Mr. Tompkins to the dignity of her mourning apparel. Obviously her mourning was becoming. It was supplying dignity and a status that she lacked. It was "a bit of class." She was one with that reserved and silent retinue of bereaved women who were dismissed as widows by those who only half-comprehended the dignity of their position. They were—Mr. Tompkins' widows were—members of a class for whom widows' weeds were nicely graded to express degrees of convalesence from inconsolable grief that Time only could heal. And Time had his favors in progressive shades born on the bonnets of the bereaved: the white, the purple, and the grey. She made a mental resolve while waiting for her old clothes to be parceled, to slip back to-morrow without her escort, and consult Miss Thorpe about acquiring half a dozen bonnets. Mr. Tompkins would be a touchstone by which to gauge their effect. She would also acquire veils of different densities and lengths. Would Mrs. Shabedge oblige by taking the parcel if they did not want it delivered? No, they did not want it delivered for the concealed reason that that would betray their address and undo the profound impression her costume or its becomingness had produced on Mr. Tompkins.

Back in her villa she practised different attitudes of dejection before her cheval glass for about a week. As she had no idea when a widow could with propriety emerge from the house of mourning, she made up her mind to go out after sundown and consult Estelle, who was not only the best fortune teller in the district, but an authority on matters of propriety and good taste. She would have her fortune told, for it would never do to pick Estelle's brains for advice about decorum without a little monetary transaction first.

What Estelle saw in the crystal, the report did not tell. If given to guessing, one might opine that it was only a foreword or a "trailer" to what was to come now that Estelle had satisfied herself about the immediate circumstances of her client. It seemed that, in order to ascertain the trend of future events, Estelle had to go into a trance. But that would take a little time, for she was not as yet fully recovered from the trance she had had to go into in order to prognosticate the amorous future of the Duchess of Stony Stratford. Would Jemima come back on Wednesday? A lucky day in spite of its being so often chosen to celebrate a certain sacrament; a lucky day, judging by Jemima's birthday. By that time she hoped that she would be in a position to tell Jemima "wot was a-comin' to her." Meanwhile, she could not see anything against the propriety of Jemima showing herself, "but not after four o'clock when they all goes home for tea," in Bond Street, or Regent Street, or even Oxford Street, "but not too far up."

Some weeks later Jemima and Florrie had a consultation after the cook left. Regrettable as it was, especially in a house of mourning, Mrs. Shabedge "gave notice" which consisted in walking out of the house into a waiting cab. Her trunk was already in the hall waiting for the cabby to put it on top. Before leaving, she assured Jemima that she had seen lots of them, but they allus had to go back to work in the end, adding "You needn't arsk me, not nohow," which was dissuading enough. This disharmony in the villa arose out of a question about the custody of the key to the cellar. Let us leave Mrs. Shabedge without regret, for from what we have seen, it is obvious that her uncouthness and lack of good breeding could not have been without an effect on the decorum of the St. John's Wood household in the end. .

After a long discourse and demonstration, Florrie had her way. They were to enlist the spare rooms of the villa in paying the taxes and the rent. For this purpose, Florrie proposed a few boarders for whom she was prepared to go bail. One was a medical student from St. Thomas's Hospital which, as it was over against Scotland Yard, seemed to convey a guarantee if not of circumspectness, at least of no departure from lawfulness. Florrie knew an artist who might come when he sold a picture— the sale was to materialize the moment that the public realized that a knowledge of drawing detracts from the fuller expression of emotion on canvas. His friend, whose beard was unkempt because he was writing *vers libre*, was refused accommodation. He might bring in a friend or two "of an evening."

Jemima's mourning kept even the medical student at bay. In addition to her mourning Jemima developed eye trouble which ringed her eyes with red. The medical student diagnosed blepharitis, and prescribed a well-advertised eye ointment and two extra glasses of whiskey before retiring.

When it was time to see Estelle, she showed her her eyes. That wise woman said, "Mockin' is catchin'," and proceeded to recount the message received in trance. You might notice 'ow pale she was from it still. She explained to Jemima, "I can't make it 'alf out. But then you never shouldn't. Taike it and maike it out for yerself. You need not arsk Estelle wot's only a medium like from the 'Igher Powers. Yes, it's five guineas. It took more out of me than that."

Jemima could hardly get home quickly enough. She ran up to her bedroom, locked the door and, without sitting down, removed a piece of tissue paper from the little envelope. The message was in writing intended to be old fashioned like the writing over the door of a recently built church. She unfolded the paper and read:

A MAN IN UNIFORM UNDER GLASS

Now what could that mean? It was no use to inquire at the source. She had been told not to arsk Estelle. It might turn the future against her if she exhibited the curiosity that was nearly always the undoing of too insistent inquirers in the fairy tales. She would ask Florrie, but that was unsatisfactory, for Florrie wanted to cross-examine her as to what was in her mind at the moment of consulting the Sibyl. There was nothing left for her but to wait and see, as the politicians do.

The experiment of the lodgers was a success, at least from Florrie's standpoint. Jemima's mourning saved its wearer from any advances, and she grew in dignity thereby. There was a lot to be said for mourning, if not for the house of mourning. Two of the hansom-driven visitors, portly and worthy citizens who were visitors to the villas

on either side, were greatly edified by the lady in mourning, and were undiplomatic enough to express their admiration to the denizens of their separate establishments.
It is to be suspected, however unworthy the thought may
be, that the ladies took these encomiums as reflections
upon themselves and resolved to have the exemplar of
sweet melancholy removed from the neighborhood. Be that
as it may, Jemima was the victim, if not of a raid, of a
domiciliary visit from the police. Jemima was admonished
and requested that, if it were necessary to take boarders,
to take them for longer terms than one night or a weekend. To crown all, Jemima imagined herself, in spite of
her weeds, cut by the policeman who used to be a frequent
visitor to the basement when Mrs. Shabedge was cook.
After a few months, she and Florrie removed to Finborough Road.

In Finborough Road, mourning was a novelty. Many
women much older and more bereaved than Jemima, wondered why they had not thought of it before. But her
mode of living was altered. Florrie, instead of continuing
as her maid and companion, was driven by the custom of
her habitat to be more or less a rival of Jemima. So
Jemima had to fend for herself and keep her apartment
worthy of the occasion when she should meet the Man in
Uniform. Every second or third day she took the bus to
the Crystal Palace, and when that egregious structure was
burned down, Jemima was at a loss. Where was there any
glass under which she might meet men in uniform? True,
in the Bunch of Grapes there was a dome of many-colored
glass and a door of the same color scheme that gave on a

room reserved for "Gentlemen." Nevertheless, Jemima knew that she was not likely to meet gentlemen in the Bunch of Grapes. There were soldiers, but not of a rank to be thought of in the same category as her friend whose livery she was still wearing. They called her "The Widow" on Finborough Road.

In summer she wore grey with white cuffs and a demure white ruffle at the neck. Her costume was as simple and restrained as her grief. In autumn she wore a little insertion of puce in her bodice and a little purple in her hat. With the lapse of years this was noticed by the policeman at the corner—the same maybe who contributed to the report—and he also noticed that sometimes in summer when he had come to expect grey, Jemima was covered from top to toe in crepe, and so heavily veiled as to be unrecognizable were it not for the veils themselves. It dawned on the observer that the addition to Jemima's mourning coincided with the deaths of well-known merchant princes or men of distinction in the state. On one occasion the morning papers extended their obituary notices to report the circumstances of the sudden death of Sir Thomas Topham, who had been found dead in the bed of a poor relation in the house next door to Jemima's old villa in St. John's Wood. Lady Topham, though well aware of the wide philanthropy of her late husband, had no knowledge of any deserving niece at that address. She was forced to conclude, and the papers followed her, that the niece in question was a brother's or sister's natural child. Thus the hint of one scandal canceled the other, and enhanced the reputation of the late Sir Thomas who did good by stealth and died before he could blush to find it in double leads. For him, if it were actually for him, Jemima's mourning was of the second class.

When the Lord Mayor of London died, a cab, its roof covered with wreaths of forget-me-nots, was seen leaving Jemima's door. She herself did not appear at the Mansion House, for she did not rise till late. For two days she remained indoors, and when she did emerge, her countenance and clothes bore the signs and symbols of profound grief.

Here it behooves us to give Florrie her due. It was she who reported that the lounge in Skindles was covered with glass. This necessitated a visit by Jemima, who was thus out of town for some days, for the place was twenty miles and more beyond London and besides, it was under "new and attentive management." As the years passed, Jemima began to feel the effect of exposure to the cold winds that blew through the railings of the Green Park. Florrie arranged with certain of her sisters to effect an exchange with the lady whose fief was the Burlington Arcade. To her they suggested that, if she gave Jemima her right to the covered arcade, she would be permitted to turn her attention exclusively to the east side of Sackville Street and one side of the street that led from it into Bond Street. Thus it was that Jemima came to enjoy the shelter of Burlington Arcade. Situated as it was between Piccadilly and the Leicester Lounge, it was considered a desirable sphere of influence.

The London bobby is full of good nature. On beat the policeman, in his night uniform and dark helmet as dark and as unreflecting as Jemima's mourning, would pass her the time of night with a jocular quizzing. " 'Aven't you got over him yet?" On such occasions Jemima would rise to the full height of her dignity and sweep past him as one not deigning to reply. At the Cork Street end, when the bobby met the sergeant, after saluting he would touch his forehead under his helmet and jerk his thumb in Jemima's direction. Often as not the sergeant would remark, "Yes, poor old soul."

Under the stairs in the St. James's Club, which is the world's center of information, Algernon Offchild would ask a companion who the widow was who had a beat in the Burlington Arcade. "Saw her last night as I was toddling to my rooms. See her every night I am not too late. She must have been a stunner in her day. Never tries to pick me up."

And so Jemima maintained the self-respect which Mr. Tompkins' "taiste" conferred to her twenty-odd years agone.

One night Platt, the policeman, declared to Sergeant Sugrue: "I didn't 'ave to read *The Evening Standard* this evening. I knew His Lordship had taken the count. Gor blimey, Lipton couldn't have caught up with her veil blowing like a balloon jib." And the sergeant laughed tolerantly.

But some months subsequently, neither Platt nor the sergeant knew whether to laugh or "to take action." The morning papers had this notice: "Sir Basil Bullfinch, Chief Commissioner of Police and ex-officio Head of Scotland Yard, passed away late last night in the sixty-fourth year of his age and the nineteenth year of his Commission, to the inexpressible grief of his family, and to the great regret of all the Force, by which body he was held in the highest esteem."

However inept his family may have been in expressing grief, Jemima was quite competent to express it. She discarded her rouge and appeared as pale as Dido under the sooty roof of the Burlington Arcade.

" 'Ow's that?" asked Constable Platt. The sergeant, who had been long enough in the Force to expect promotion and to suspect his superior, said, as one who wished to give the Commissioner the benefit of the doubt, "Well, I wouldn't put it past him." Then, with the detachment of an oracle, "You never can tell."

As she declined in years and charm, Jemima all the more exalted her past. The mourning she assumed at the loss of her first lover was continued, until at length she came to mourn her lover in every lover whom she thought worthy of ranking with her paragon. This state of mind is nothing new, but as old as human nature. The only hope for one who has no future is to magnify the past. Is there an aging man but wishes to live again in the time of his achievement?

In London a thing that begins as a joke or a laughing stock often ends by being accepted, taken seriously, and clothed with respect, provided it has been in existence long enough. The name of the late Mr. Deniges' firm of attorneys is an example. Once a thing is established, it partakes of the repute that comes to a business from the mere fact of its continuance. Long before she became one of those minor and surreptitious interests of the town, the kind that interest pressmen but never get into the press, Jemima was accepted. As a result of this, she almost ceased to attract attention until one day, or evening rather. On the morning of this momentous day, the papers came out in heavy leads. There were black borders between the columns of the front page. The length of the time the Court would go into mourning as a result of the sad news they announced was published. Sporting fixtures (for the day) were called off. His Majesty, on account of his bereavement, would not proceed to Scotland though a portrait of his grandmother, the good Queen, hung all over the railway station. Levity at this moment would be in the worst possible taste. Nobody smiled even under the stairs of the St. James Club. But Jemima—who could accuse her of levity? And yet Sergeant Sugrue agreed with Constable Platt that she was going a bit too far. "You can have too much of a good thing" he said referring to that embodiment of grief.

But what would the charge be if they ran Jemima into Vine Street. You cannot accuse a loyal citizen who joined a nation in mourning of *lese majesté* in spite of what Sergeant Sugrue described as "the 'orrible hinnuendo of the thing." The law was in a quandary. So was the sergeant. Respectability rules Britannia. Respectability came to his aid.

The first thing to do was to get her off the streets. "Wot about taking her into custody?"

Constable Platt was embarrassed. "You are not going to arrest her?" Then he remembered that he was addressing a superior officer: "Excuse me, sir, but it would be easier on her if you was to take her into custody. It would give her more of an honor like."

"Now Platt," said the sergeant speaking authoritatively, "I'm a married man. You go along and take her quietly. I will move along and speak to the officer at the desk."

Under the glazed roof of that tunnel which is Burlington Arcade, Jemima saw the constable advancing. As he approached, he drew off his glove. Thus it came about that Jemima met a man in uniform under glass.

Later, in the station, the constable in charge asked in the manner of those who make a charge when propounding a question: "Wot's all this I hear about His Royal Highness?" Jemima bent her head still lower than her grief had bowed it. From her reticule she drew a handkerchief bordered with a wide band of black, a thing undreamt of and unforeseen by that costumier of woe, Mr. Tompkins, years and years in the past. With it she covered her face. The sergeant produced a chair. On this Jemima sat, too convulsed with tears to reply. The tears she shed were for all lovers since the beginning of Love's eventful history, tears salt as the waves that drowned Leander, tears bitter as the sea from which the Mother of Love arose. Tears for youth's distress amid misunderstandings, tears for the tragedy that is inseparable from passion, tears for her own lost love and youth. The weeds of mourning that became Mrs. Spendlove or, rather, the clothes by which she became "Mrs." when she was married posthumously, so to speak, did not cease to favor her now.

Behind her veil her eyes tear-bright seemed to deepen, and the swelling that had been caused by her tears had the effect of removing the little wrinkles that might have given a look of age to her face. The policemen were surprised; they looked at each other as if the other was responsible for giving a wrong impression of Mrs. Spendlove's age. At the desk the sergeant whispered, "We cannot hold her for being in mourning. The Court is in mourning. Enter nothing on the sheet." He closed his ledger and dismissed the constable with, "It's up to you to handle her. You ran her in." So saying, he went out to lunch, leaving Constable Platt alone with Mrs. Spendlove in the inner room.

"There, there," said the constable to Mrs. Spendlove as soothingly as is possible for a man in uniform to speak. "You can go home in a minute, as soon as the crowd goes away. The sergeant says that you can wear anything you like, and I'm not saying that what you are wearing now isn't becoming. It suits you fine."

Twisted Oliver   THE EMBARRASSMENT
OF BARCLAY MEDLICOTT, TOLD BY HIMSELF

$\mathcal{F}ew$ MEN ARE WORTHY OF leisure, and leisure I discovered when I retired from the Inorganic Bank.

I had been granted a pension which permitted me to live in dignified comfort, without ostentation, in conformity with my status as a banker and the tradition of our Bank. I decided to give up my house on Long Island and move into the city where, I opined, the bustle and distraction would, in its way, carry me over the period of transition that must elapse before I could adjust myself to a change of the rhythm, so to speak, to which I had been accustomed for upwards of forty years. This was effected without undue complications thanks to the devotion of my housekeeper, who not only directed the removal of my furniture, but followed me to my new home.

I chose an apartment building on Park Avenue in the sixties. It was not a modern building by any means; but this was compensated by the solidity of its construction, its spaciousness, and by what is hard to define for one to whom writing does not come with the facility of figures:

its atmosphere of social composure. To all appearances those who lived in it had been in residence for years. There was a feeling of continuance about the building that I felt would impart to me the sense of security that I had lost on retiring from a well-established and respectable institution.

I had not been in possesssion of my new apartments for more than a few weeks until I discovered that it was possible to fall into a routine. I would walk, for instance, every morning down the Avenue to Forty-fifth or Forty-sixth Street and turn east to see the sun balanced upon its rim in the middle of the street. This phenomenon gave me an aesthetic pleasure and made me feel commiseration for those lie-a-beds who miss so much of the natural beauty that arises from the play of light on the towers and spires of New York. The pigeons that haunt the gables of the churches no doubt got to know me and to expect some little morsel of food that I made a point of carrying. Pigeons, I mused, have a tradition that associates them with the Temple of Solomon. How appropriate therefore is their association with the churches of the present day.

After some months in the apartment building, I made one or two acquaintances. The first was a lady who had a friend in common with me. This pleasantly surprising discovery I made one afternoon when the friend called to consult me about a matter of bank business and to benefit by the advice which my long connection with the Bank had entitled him to expect. Perhaps here I should state, though it may appear to be a confession of a certain kind of weakness, that I rented a safety deposit box on leaving

the Bank so that my association of forty years might not
be too abruptly and completely broken. Among the personal treasures I kept there, the most prized was an illu-
minated address that accompanied a presentation at the
dinner given in my honor on the occasion of my resigna-
tion.

To the lady thus introduced to me, I in turn presented
the widow of a lifelong friend, and between them the
ladies found out that several of the denizens of our building were friends or acquaintances of theirs, members of
the adjoining Colony Club. We exchanged visits at regular intervals, and on one occasion I permitted myself to
give a little dinner in their honor, and in celebration of
the peaceful leisure to which I was committed for the re-
mainder of my life. We would play a little game of cards
after dinner on those occasions when the ladies did not
prefer their own conversation to my bridge. While they
talked I played patience and consoled myself for the
apparent incivility with the thought that I had begun to
be regarded by them as a familiar acquaintance, one in
whose presence a little liberty might be taken without
causing offence. I was a poor card player. And I was
dependent on them for their society. Until one day I made
an acquaintance of my own.

It came about in this way. My apartment was on the
seventh floor; that of my new acquaintance on the sixth.
One afternoon the operator, to whom I was the better
known, inadvertently took us up beyond the landing of
the sixth-floor lady. When I discovered the mistake, I refused to avail myself of it; I remained in the elevator until

it descended and took the lady to her own floor. This little courtesy was reciprocated by a polite word of thanks and the expression of a wish that, as we were tenants of the same building, we might not remain unacquainted with one another.

On the following day the elevator operator brought me a note. If I were free any evening I would be welcome to join my new acquaintance—her name was Mrs. Rhinelander—and her friends in a game of bridge. It appeared that she devoted quite a little time to instructing young persons in that intricate game. I accepted the invitation, for I had resolved to become more expert, and, having allowed an appropriate interval to elapse, presented myself one evening at her apartment. She introduced herself: "Mrs. Alice Rhinelander." I named myself in my turn, "Barclay Medlicott, late of the Inorganic Bank."

The dining room was devoted to cards. Some of her friends, all of whom were young ladies, played with us or in the living room from which I could hear their joyous laughter from time to time. I inquired if my hostess were a follower of Culbertson, but she shook her head and said that she had a system of her own which, if I adopted it, would make me as expert as any player I would be likely to meet. I had confessed to her that my attempts to play bridge were not taken very seriously by my opponents, who seemed to find more entertainment in general conversation.

As the evenings progressed, in spite of my absorption in the game, I noticed at times when the telephone rang that our younger partners would often beg to be excused.

Though this caused an interruption, it was easily adjusted and we proceeded as if no interruption had occurred. It gave me a chance to become known to them all and the association thus created reacted favorably on me. I found myself rejuvenated to some extent by the presence of young people. Though they had hardly the disposition to become serious players, their vivacity and cheerfulness were ample compensation.

I was making such progress that I resolved to keep my visits and the source of my knowledge hidden until the time should come when I could surprise my older friends. To preserve my secret all the more securely I availed myself of the marble stairway instead of the elevator to visit Mrs. Rhinelander's apartment on the floor beneath mine.

One evening I was partnered by an older player, a Mme K. Jamyn, who had come recently from Paris on the Gripsholm. She was a sister of my hostess, evidently a woman of some judgment, a *femme du monde* who, in spite of the atrocious occupation of Paris, spoke without bitterness of the German garrison of the city that was so long her home.

As the evening advanced, the telephone calls increased, and one night there were three calls in quick succession that caused three exits of our fair young friends, whose parents, I imagined, were growing anxious, as they might justly be. But to my surprise the three young ladies who had answered the telephone all returned within a short time. I had not remarked this before. Hitherto whoever went out had stayed away for a considerable time or had not returned. These three young ladies seemed to have some important message for Mrs. Rhinelander. After an interval of confused whispering, I heard Mme Jamyn's voice raised authoritatively, saying to her sister in our colloquial English, "Let me handle this." Whereupon she left and the game was ended for the evening.

This I did not regret because, sitting as I was with one shoulder towards the radiator and the other towards the window, I was growing increasingly uneasy lest the unequal temperature bring on an attack of neuritis. They say that fear precipitates whatever disease we dread. Suffice it to say that my card games and the many shiftings of positions involved by the disappearance of the partners brought on a sharp attack of neuritis or bursitis, which caused me to go for nearly all the month of January to Hot Springs, Virginia.

When an addict to drink becomes a teetotaller, many little disabilities that passed unnoticed while he was drinking rear their heads and make themselves manifest during his period of abstinence. This is what I have been told. Though it is rather an inappropriate simile, I noticed that when I was reduced to inaction during my convalescence, time hung heavily on my hands. The alacrity with which I returned to New York as soon as my discomfort had decreased was a measure of my ennui.

The doorman was delighted to see me and he inquired solicitously about the state of my health. Such little considerations give an apartment building the atmosphere of a home. In turn I asked after my new friends. The question was apparently disconcerting. He became undisguisedly reticent. With awakening apprehension I asked outright if any of them were dead.

"Much worse," he said, shaking his head.

"Much worse! What do you mean? Speak out, my good man!"

He began reluctantly but soon unburdened his mind. There had been a raid, proceedings in court, the summoning of witnesses and a sentence on my instructress of bridge. . . .

"I have kept the papers. Perhaps you would like to read them."

To this I was about to answer, "But what have I to do with it?" when I realized that it was incumbent on me to acquaint myself with all the facts of the case before I adopted any attitude. Besides, I am not in favor of dissimulation of any kind. So I accepted the clippings with a word of thanks for his consideration.

When I was settled in my apartment, what I read amazed me. I was horrified as I fitted in retrospect every link of what, at the time, had seemed to me so innocent, but was now so obnoxious. Mrs. Rhinelander's name was assumed; it was the name of the telephone exchange of what was in reality a "house of call." My bright young companions were nothing better—than . . . A wave of comfort came over me as I recalled the steps that I had taken to conceal my new acquaintances from my other neighbors until I should be sufficiently proficient in the game of bridge. Then I remembered the doorman's words about witnesses. Had I been sought for? If so, what did my life-long friend's widow think of me? What would my old colleagues at the Bank think? The very fact that my visits were clandestine would be turned against me. I could hardly bring myself to read further. Yet I had to read on. I owed it to myself.

Three girls were examined first. They gave their ages as 18, 19 and 17½ and their address was the same as mine! They testified that a call came to Rhinelander —— from a commercial hotel near by, the Belldome, to be exact. The caller gave the number of his floor and the number of his room. The youngest, the girl called Viggy, answered it without disturbing Mrs. Rhinelander, who was playing bridge.

"With whom?"

"With her sister, Nancy and Vi."

Not a word about my presence in the apartment. In spite of this heinous trade, there was apparently, absurd as it sounds, honor among thieves or, in this case, reprobates.

"You are seventeen and a half years old. Tell the court what happened."

"When I got to the hotel, I went to the room number given. I knocked on the door and when I heard, 'Come,' I went in and saw a stocky old guy standing in the middle of the room dressed in a little boy's suit. He told me he was Oliver Twist."

"Oliver Twist?"

"That's what he said."

"How did you say he was dressed?"

"He had short socks, a little boy's pants that hardly came halfway down his thighs, a jacket, and a little hat."

Here the judge interposed and called for order and said that if there were any more levity he would have the court cleared of all but the accused, the essential witnesses, and the officials.

"And what did you do?" the prosecuting attorney asked.

"Nothing."

"Come now. Do you mean to say on your oath that you did nothing when you saw this half naked man in the room?"

This brought a protest from the defense and "half naked" was disallowed. The prosecutor resumed.

"Why did you do nothing?"

"He told me to go home. He said I was too young."

Exactly the same evidence was adduced from the two other young women, whom I remembered so well going out that night and returning shortly later in confusion.

The hotel detective was then called to the stand. His testimony chiefly concerned Mme Jamyn. He had seen her enter the room and had taken his post outside the door. He deposed that when she walked into the room and saw the man who told her he was Oliver Twist, without a moment's hesitation she shouted:

"You are a bad boy! How dare you put on your best suit without permission?"

"What then?" the witness was asked.

"He said he thought it was Sunday; that he guessed he was a bad boy but hoped he would not be spanked.

" 'Spanked?' said the woman. 'Of course you will be spanked. Come here this minute.'

"After a pause I heard sounds of slapping and then the woman said, 'Stand over there in the corner until I tell you to move.' Then acting on instructions, I broke into the room and found the defendant standing in one corner of the room over near the window with his face turned to the wall."

I glanced ahead down the column, but nowhere did my name catch my eye. I was able to read the defense with more equanimity than I could bring to bear on the prosecution. There was some argument as to what constitutes moral turpitude. Then the defense took a strange turn. It seems that such aberrations of human behaviour were well known to psychiatrists; perversions, they were termed. The psychiatrist who gave evidence quoted a German professor, one Sigmund Freud, whereupon the judge addressed the jury.

"Authorities, as these psychiatrists are called, may be authorities on their own subject; but you must bear in mind that they have invented that subject and presented it in such a way as to absolve the victim or pervert of all responsibility. They would seem to obliterate the distinctions between good and evil, right and wrong, and make this odious behaviour appear as if it were the result of forces hidden in the unconscious mind of the victim. This is a most wicked and reprehensible trick. Freud may be a prophet in his own country—which probably deserves what it gets—but he is not a prophet in this country and his poisonous doctrines are not admissible as evidence in this court. I consider Freud and all his followers enemies of the human race. . . ."

Twisted Oliver

What a rock was this honorable judge in a welter of
vicious nonsense!

I put down the paper and began to ponder my own
position in relation to this unfortunate affair. One by one
I considered the residents of the building with whom I was
acquainted. It was quite apparent to me that I could
hardly ask my friend Mrs. Toinbee, Jr., who must not be
confused with the Racine Toinbees, whether she knew of
my association with the—house of call—on the sixth floor,
even though such association was accidental and innocent. Nor could I very well put that question to Mrs.
de Gaudens, the authority on the Corniche Road; nor to
Mr. Piper, an inconsiderable fellow, that is if anyone can
be called inconsiderable who can, with a word, take away
one's good name and life-long repute for integrity.

But the Bank—my Bank? I anticipated the unkind
jokes the junior members of that institution might make
at my expense. They would ask each other how I had
found out such an iniquitous habitation. They might even,
if anyone could be so unjust, tell each other that my
choice of residence went far to explain why I had never
married.

Mrs. Pritchard, my housekeeper, was the unknowing
source of great comfort to me at this distressing time.
This excellent woman was, in common with many other
ancillaries, a receptacle for the continuous gossip that
goes on in any large building where many persons of different avocations are housed. She revealed to me that the
servants of the building took the gossip more to heart
than did the tenants, many of whom, and this included all

my acquaintances, were unaware that they were under the same roof that had sheltered Mrs. Rhinelander. I came to the conclusion that all I had to fear was possibly an anonymous letter, perhaps from some clerk whom I might have found it necessary to reprimand in the past. But no decent person should or would take anything that is anonymous into account. However to distract myself, I visited the Planetarium where in the presence of cosmic immensities the petty troubles of our planet are readily discounted. I soon felt calmed and less apprehensive, and I returned with an appetite to do justice to Mrs. Pritchard's adequate cuisine.

To my relief and gratification my confidence and composure were fully restored to me on the following day by a letter which came from the Bank and which, for an unpleasant moment, I hesitated to open. But my apprehensions were groundless and with a deep feeling of intense satisfaction I read a most courteous and charming letter from the Bank inviting me to become one of their Board of Directors as from the first day of the fiscal year.

That morning I went down in the elevator with a high heart. The gloom that I had felt to be superincumbent on the building had lifted. The doorman had recovered from his concern and even attempted to turn the scandal into an unbecoming joke. "Madame had the situation well in hand!" This levity I treated as it deserved, that is by disregarding it.

I walked down the Avenue. The sun shone on the spire of the Chrysler Building as it gleamed in the clear air beside and beyond the towers of the Waldorf. With my eyes fixed on the lofty roofs of the city I failed to see the leash of a small dog that crossed my path. It was led by a young woman who eyed me without the decorum I was entitled to expect of a resident of a locality such as ours. I ignored her completely and set my face steadfastly towards the Inorganic Bank.

James Joyce: A Portrait of the Artist

A Young MAN SAT BESIDE me in the electric tram as it sped up the slight incline of Rutland Square on its way towards Glasnevin. I had been introduced to him by some student friend so casually that to speak to him again was like introducing myself. I could see his clear profile with its straight nose that came out at an angle from a towering forehead. The skin of his face was thick and ruddy seen through the down of a golden beard. His eyelashes were long and chestnut colored, flat at the roots as they swept upward over smoke-gray, clouded eyes. He weighed about one hundred twenty-five pounds, if as much as that, for he was very slender. When he stood up, he was about my own height, which is five feet nine. In his hand he carried a roll of manuscript tied with a piece of string.

"You are Mr. Joyce?" I ventured.

There was no reply. I felt embarrassed until I realized that his silence was due to a shyness as great as the diffidence of a lay brother in a monastery.

I was a Trinity College man, and Trinity College, being its only college, is synonymous with Dublin University.

Joyce was attending classes given by the Jesuits in the great house where had dwelt Buck Whaley, one of those characters in whom the eighteenth century flared up and went out. As a 'Varsity man I had to be regarded, in self-defense, as a scion of the Ascendancy. Joyce's defensive attitude later assumed fantastic proportions.

I tried again: "Are you going in my direction?"

"Apparently."

It was not very promising but the silence was broken.

"I live near the Botanic Gardens. Where do you live?"

"Cabra."

"I hope that they are poems that you have there?" I said, pointing to the roll of vellum.

"They are," he asserted with a trace of challenge.

Such was the kernel from which our friendship grew.

I remember that it was spring because, when we walked in my garden weeks later, the apple trees were in bloom, and there is bloom in the first of the lyrics he reluctantly showed me. His manuscript consisted of twenty large pages. In the middle of each page was a little lyric that looked all the more dainty from the beautiful handwriting in which it was written; Tennysonian, exquisite things:

> My love is in a light attire
> Among the apple trees
> Where the young winds do most desire
> To run in companies.

We walked in that garden for many eager days. We talked of the poets, Yeats, Mangan, Ferguson, and George Russell. Only the dead were commendable to Joyce.

One morning in the middle of one of my dissertations, "Will you lend me your rifle?" he interrupted.

This was rather disconcerting because I thought that I was talking rather well and agreeing with him by admiring Mangan's "Veil not thy mirror, sweet Amine," to which he had drawn my attention some days previously. Besides, he was anything but a sportsman; yet, full of curiosity, I lent him my .22.

Not long afterward, he came to me as enthusiastic as he ever permitted himself to be. He had a great idea. He would rent the Martello Tower out at Sandy-cove. I would furnish it, and we would live defiantly and far from the madding crowd.

Now the Martello Tower was one of the many stone fortresses that the British government in the days of Napoleon built, characteristically, *after* the alarm of invasion was over. The south coast of England and the southeast coast of Ireland were studded with them. Nine or ten of them guarded Dublin Bay, even where landing was impossible.

The one we took was built of cut granite and shaped like a sculptor's mallet, from which the name "martello" is said to be derived. It stood over the Forty Foot, a bathing pool in the granite cliffs about six or seven miles south of Dublin. It was entered by a ladder to a door halfway up the wall on the side farthest from the sea.

We went together to see it. Joyce produced a very large copper key about ten inches long. The door had not been opened for years, so we had some difficulty in getting in. At last the great metal door was opened. We descended a few steps and entered a large circular room. There was a clamor of wings as some pigeons flew up through the embrasures of the little windows. The roof was a strong cylinder of stone. Around the room went a deep shelf at arms' reach. A fireplace was opposite to the door. On the left side we saw a little door and, opening it, discovered a flight of steps in the thickness of the wall. Full of adventure we ascended. What a pleasant discovery! There was a platform of granite and a circular raised wall from which you could see over the battlements head high. There was the Hill of Howth that formed the northern arm of Dublin Bay lying purple in the light. Dublin lay to the west, a dull ruby under a canopy of smoke. The sight fascinated Joyce. For a long time he gazed at his native town, "The Seventh City of Christendom."

I was looking at Killiney Hill, the south guardian of the Bay. I rejoiced at the green, the deep green of the Hill where its cliffs of granite were climbed by pines.

"This will do for a table," Joyce said, pointing to the gun emplacement, "and we can sit in the step and move around with the sun. We can do as much sun-bathing as we wish. Nobody can see us here. We can see everyone when we look over the parapet."

It was true. I looked over the parapet. I could see men bathing in the Forty Foot. I could see old Carson's sunburned body rolling in the waves on his way back from his two-mile swim to the Muglins. I could see Lyons and Jem, the fishermen, sitting under the Battery wall. We overlooked everything from our seventy-foot eminence.

When we were returning to the big room, we missed the

door in the darkness and reached a semicircular cellar which had a copper-lined powder store and a cistern for water from the roof.

"We could stand a siege here," Joyce remarked.

"It's a good retreat for those who like retreating."

"We must take possession at once until you get in the furniture. Could you do it today?"

"I thought we had possession. Haven't you got the key?"

Joyce had an uncle who was a clerk in an attorney's office, and from him Joyce got a respect for the formalities of law.

"We must leave something here until we move in."

When we ascended to the living room, very formally Joyce "took possession" by laying his roll of poems on the shelf.

I was so delighted by the discovery of a residence that could be locked and left secure for a half a year if necessary, that I lost no time in getting beds, tables, chairs, utensils, washing basins, and fish kettles, and everything else that I could think of from my home. They were carted down next day.

The fishermen were set to clean out all vestiges that the wild pigeons had left and to put the place shipshape. Joyce's bed was to the right of the door, mine to the left. We had a table directly under one of the two window shafts where the light fell. The cooking things were piled up on the wide shelf to the right.

Joyce, who had once or twice said that he was suffering from inanition, had no fear of inanition now. Lobsters could be bought from the obliging Lyons or the morose Jem for twelve cents each, and mackerel for a cent each or two for a cent if they were not large. Milk, butter, and eggs were so cheap that we could save for those nutritious pints of Guinness without which half Dublin would be half-starved.

Mr. Murray who kept "Murray's," the local tavern, was a blear-eyed little man with a broad forehead and a thin neck. His house was next to the railway arch, so, when he helped his clients, he could truthfully say, "This is the best pint between this and 'The Arch,' " which was a well-known tavern seven miles away. When his wife died, a paraphrase from *Lycidas*, "She must not float upon his watery beer, Unwept," drew a thin smile from the lips of Joyce.

The problem of how to live without having to go to town every day Joyce solved by taking a job as a teacher in a neighboring school. He had, at first, thought of forming himself into a company, the shareholders in which were to receive all the proceeds from his future writings. The idea was novel. The shareholders would have to keep and humor him. Already, I said, I could see them issuing an unbalanced sheet. It was left to the British government to invest the royal bounty of $500 a year in him, and to a Mrs. Weaver, later, to put $100,000 into that stock. There were worse investments than in James Joyce, Inc.

At last all was ready. The fishermen had gone, the milk had been delivered. We had eggs and bacon in store. Joyce sighed with relief.

"What will we do now?" he asked.

"The first thing to do is to let me get rid of your beard," I said. "There is lovely soft water in the storage tank and we should use it even if it's too old to drink. You can offer up your whiskers to the Muses."

It took very little persuasion because to use water from our own storage tank appealed to him. So I shaved Joyce for the first time in his life when, as Homer says, "the youth of man is most comely." He never forgot it, for, when he paid me the only kind of compliment he ever paid, and that is to mention a person in his writings, he described me shaving on the top of the tower. In fact, I am the only character in all his works who washes, shaves, and swims.

Many friends bearing gifts came to stay with us for week ends. We had much to offer, for we were possessed of the freshest air nearest to the city. We could and did feast on the roof, using, as Joyce had at first suggested, the gun emplacement for a table. The gun had gone with its company long long ago.

We had at hand the best cure for any little indisposition that remained from overnight, a dive down and down through the green water of the Forty Foot, then breakfast of ham and eggs.

The insoluble problem of cleaning up and getting rid of grease was at last solved by me. Instead of spreading grease all over the crockery in the wash basin while trying to get it off a plate or two, I used metal plates and put them in the fire until they were sterilized, a method of dry cleaning that has been too long forgotten.

In our talks, Joyce laid down many rules for good writing. I wish I had listened and had not talked so much. One was, "Don't exaggerate. Tell the truth." Another, "Describe what they do."

When he could, he spent his time in the National Library. Here he taught himself Danish. It was little trouble to him to acquire a language. His memory was marvelous, and he had a good ear. He was also skilled in music. He once wrote me a letter in which he told of a plan to tour the coastwise towns of England singing old English ballads to the accompaniment of a lute by Dolmnetsch. That was in 1904. A singer has made a fortune by doing that very thing in recent years. Joyce's voice was clarion clear. John McCormack may not have heard it, for he described it as baritone. It was tenor. He would have won first prize at the Feis, which is the annual musical festival and competition, that year but for his bad sight that prevented him scoring at sight singing. As it was, he got the bronze medal which indignantly he threw into the Liffey.

Joyce at that time was undergoing an inward change which may explain some of his curious behavior. Revolt and scorn were increasing within him as he brooded and pondered over *Ulysses*. He was the storm-tossed wanderer whose ingenuity would bring him to his kingdom. He was Stephen Daedalus, the crowned and curious artist. With Prussian strategy he defended himself by attacking. On Yeats's fortieth birthday he called on the poet, who was staying at the Cavendish Hotel. I give the account of this incident as I heard it.

After some ceremony, Joyce was admitted. "How old are you?" he asked Yeats, although he must have known well Yeats's age from the newspaper accounts.

"This is my birthday. I am forty years old," Yeats replied.

"Sorry. You are too old for me to help," Joyce said insolently and turned on his heel. The incident impressed Yeats more than it offended him. He was enchanted by Joyce's eccentricity and audacity, though he did not suspect how far from being audacity it was in reality. But personalities could never affect Yeats's admiration for genius. It was he and Ezra Pound who secured from Mr. Asquith for Joyce, who was then in Zurich, the royal bounty already mentioned. Of *Ulysses* Yeats wrote, "The Martello Tower pages are full of beauty, a cruel, playful mind like a great, soft tiger cat."

When I looked for the hidden model whom Joyce was imitating I was puzzled for a time, though I knew well that there must be some literary figure, probably beyond my ken, whom Joyce admired. At last I had it! Rimbaud. I remembered how he would quote Rimbaud. I remember Rimbaud's revolt not only against the accepted forms of literature, but against language itself. Rimbaud! No one who studies Joyce should neglect this clue to his character and conduct at the time. And the time was 1905. He left for Flushing at the end of the year and, sure enough, I got a postcard photograph of James Joyce dressed in a long overcoat with muffler and black soft hat. Arthur Rimbaud!

Had my knowledge of European literature been more

catholic, I would have recognized Rimbaud in Joyce sooner than I did. I had had quite a dose of Ibsen when Joyce Ibsenized himself translating the gloomy Norwegian.

Lady Gregory, who early had kidnaped Yeats and who was a disarming old lady, used as a conduit by Yeats to draw off his comic writings, had no use for Joyce. To her he was not "out of the top drawer"; and she had all the snobbery of the shoneens of Galway.

One day an SOS was issued from the Abbey Theatre. It had run out of geniuses. Joyce, as great a genius as any save Yeats himself, applied in person to Lady Gregory. I was waiting outside some place at which she was staying—I think that it was in Molesworth Street. Joyce was not in long. Presently he appeared, full of gravity, an assumption of seriousness he kept for occasions when shot full of the slings and arrows. Gravely he inclined his head. Gravely he beat time with his forefinger and recited this impromptu limerick:

> There was an old lady called "Gregory"
> Said, "Come to me, poets in beggary";
> But found her imprudence
> When thousands of students
> Cried, "All, we are in that category!"

Thus we lived in privacy and profanity. I could take it easy on the roof, for I shunned work; Joyce could remain downstairs forever reading and rereading his *Contra Gentiles*, an early essay against everybody. I never saw him put pen to paper. He would often excuse himself "to write a letter," which was his way of recording any turn of

phrase he heard, or any one of my "epiphanies," by which
he meant unconscious "giveaways." If, for instance, I said
I had no money and, later, revealed through some allusion
that I had had some all the time, that would be an epiphany
or a "showing forth," a parody on the meaning of the
church festival of that name.

This is but one example of his play on words. Why
should I give others, when there are so many in his later
works? Now, word associations and rebuses are no new
thing in Irish literature. They are indigenous to monas-
teries and schools. The schoolmen of the ninth and the
following centuries indulged in them *in excelsis*. It was in
the schools that such equivoces as *"Mea mater mala sus
est"* originated, a sentence that may be construed as "My
mother is an evil sow," or as "Hurry, Mother! The sow
is eating the apples."

As for the association of ideas in such phrases as "tight-
breeched British artilleryman," which occurs in *Gas From
a Burner*, that angry and unpublished poem he shot back
at us from Flushing, at that time he was putting legions
of them together. The Martello Tower was the nursery
of *Ulysses*.

Sometimes when I would be lolling on the roof, getting
a tan and feeling the sun pulsating on my skin, I would
think of Joyce in the dark room underneath and invite
him to come out into the air. It was no use shouting.
Nothing could be heard in that room, so it would be necessary to go down the stairs, and put my head against the
top of the door and call. I called, "Kinch! Come up. It's
a lovely day."

"Why should I go up?"

"Because you are committing the Eight Deadly Sins by being 'sullen in the sweet air.' You know what your pal Dante does with such as you?"

"Go back to your sweet air."

"Your mind will break your heart, dear Kinch."

I went back. *Why do I put up with him at all? I asked myself. It must be the attraction of opposites that holds us together. But he is a bit of a weight. It is hard to make him smile except at some blunder of mine or others. Here I am with two madmen in the Tower. Narrumtour? Am I their keeper or companion? Then there is the fact that Endymion, the madman, likes only me. "Show me your company." My uncle was said to have been very wild and to have died in America. The first part of his history may be hereditary. What am I to do?*

Kinch calls me "Malachi Mulligan." "Malachi wore the collar of gold," and he is envious of my canary-colored waistcoat with the gold buttons. Besides, "Malachi" is his way of hinting "Mercury"; and "Mulligan" is stage Irish for me and the rest of us. It is meant to make me absurd. I don't resent it, for he takes "Kinch"—"Lynch" with the Joyces of Galway, which is far worse. I might have called him "Haughton," after the grandfather of Baldy Haughton who invented the "drop" in hanging. And "Haughton" would convey to him "Haughty" or "Plaughton" and "Plutone." He would have taken that, for he intends to put us all in his underworld one of these days. Meanwhile, who ever heard of Hermes having a drink with Pluto?

One Sunday we decided to go to Dublin, for we were in funds. We would knock about for a while and, in the evening, drop in on AE's Hermetic Society, which was founded and presided over by AE (George Russell) himself. This society intrigued Joyce; he could not get into it. The majority of its members were girls who worked in Pim's, the large Quaker dry-goods store in which AE was an accountant. This was the society that George Moore and I visited years later to find AE astride a bench in a little room crowded with intense females, and in the process of digging up from the World Memory a Fifth Gospel.

When Moore heard AE, with "his fading knowledge of Hebrew" (sic), intoning "Oom" or "Amen" five times, he exclaimed impatiently, "Why he's got it upside down," an irreverence that had us both removed.

Joyce and I spent most of Sunday having quick ones in Davy Byrne's, Mooney's, Fanning's, and Kennedy's with John Elwood, Vincent Cosgrove, Sweeney, the greengrocer, and Cocky Meade. About nine o'clock we thought that the Hermetic would be in full blast. We reached the tall forbidding office building in Dawson Street by the side door in the lane that leads through an arch to South Frederick Street. It was by this door, Joyce said, that the members were wont to enter unobtrusively. We pushed it in and struggled up the dark stairway. We found the door and entered. I struck a match. The place was empty except for some deal chairs and the form or bench on which the Master rode. I saw the gas bracket and lit the burner. So this was the temple of the secret society. Joyce came upon a suitcase behind him near the door, and he opened it out of curiosity. Ribbon-tied packages were revealed. Through the tissue paper I could see gauze or muslin materials.

"Ladies' drawers," said Joyce, imitating a salesman. "Here are the latest fashions, ladies, in all tones, shapes, and sizes."

"What goes on in here?" I asked, thinking of the reputation of the Thrice Great Hermes.

"Not what you think," Joyce said. "They belong to Maunsell's manager's traveling bag. He probably arrived from Belfast only to find that the Society was not in session this Sunday. So he dumped his samples here, and will pick them up in the morning. Only he will have to sell them this week without the spiritual support of AE."

The gas from the burner went out. We stumbled down the stairs, and into the street. To my amazement, I saw that Joyce was carrying the suitcase full of ladies' underwear.

"They can pull us in for breaking and entering," I protested. "We are up against the Eighth Commandment, and it's worse on Sunday when the pawnshops are closed."

He brooded awhile and said, "If there were no pawnshops there would be no need for an Eighth Commandment."

"There are no pawnshops in the Bible," I objected.

"There are money changers, usurers, and a lot about covetousness."

"When I think of what went on in the Bible, it's just a miracle that there are only ten commandments. Never let me hear you say that I don't believe in miracles!"

"It is a miracle to believe in anything," he said.

I looked at him sharply. Was this one of his jokes? But the thin lips did not cream or wrinkle.

"What do you intend to do with them?" I said.

"I intend to present them to our lady friends with the compliments of the Hermetic Society."

I thought this over. "Give me a few dozen for Jenny."

Jenny was an acrobat and a friend of Sweeney, the greengrocer. Any little act of kindness done to Jenny (provided that it was not of love) would not be lost on Sweeney, as it certainly would not be on Jenny.

Joyce suggested that we call on Jenny with my gift, and we took a cab to Mountjoy Street. Jenny was, as always, charmed to see us. After some desultory but unedifying conversation, we opened "Maunsell's manager's traveling bag," and Joyce advanced with what should have been my present. As he bowed over its recipient his toe struck a night jar, which rang sonorously like a gong.

Jenny sat up and, as a little voluntary act of recompense, proceeded to try the undies on. The display was so edifying that Joyce threw in the rest, suitcase and all.

Later, as we sat in the last train back to Sandycove, the sea and the clear air, Joyce, who had been in a brown study, announced abruptly, "At last I've got a title for my collection of lyrics."

"What is it?" I inquired.

"*Chamber Music*," he said.

One term when I came down from Oxford, I brought to the tower a friend, a Balliol man, Samuel Chevenix Trench, an enthusiastic Gaelic speaker and, in his spare time, an amateur teacher of Gaelic, in Oxford of all places. It was with him I learned the few sentences I know. I thought that it would be an enjoyable thing for him to come to Ireland and meet the galaxy of Gaels and those who were working for a renewed Ireland: Horace Plunkett and his pet editor, George Russell, and the men who were quoting Dean Swift, "Burn everything English but her coal," in their efforts to revive Irish industries. The effect on Trench was astonishing. First of all, he applied to the courts for permission to change his name by deed poll. He became Diarmuid instead of Samuel. He grew so zealous for things made in Ireland that he went about with his shoe leather all green for want of blacking made in Ireland. He removed the shades of our lamps and filled the tower with smoke until Irish glass should appear to take their places. He upset Joyce literally and metaphorically. Joyce courteously offered his place by the door for Trench's bed and went over to the right under the large shelf with his bed.

All went well for some weeks, for we were using the tower only to sleep in, except on week ends. Trench tried but failed to convert Joyce to Gaelic, so he becomes the Englishman, Haines, in *Ulysses*, where Joyce betrays a hidden respect for what is derisively called "The Ascendancy." As for me, he makes me open *Ulysses* as Buck Mulligan shaving before a cracked mirror (by which he is supposed to symbolize Ireland) on the tower: another "buck" like Whaley.

One summer night, when it was too hot to sleep although the door was open, shortly after midnight Trench, who had been dozing, awoke suddenly and screamed, "The black panther!"

He produced a revolver and fired two or three shots in the direction of the grate. Then, exhausted, he subsided into sleep. I gently removed the gun. Joyce sat up on his elbow, overcome by consternation. Soon again, as I had guessed he would, Trench awoke and saw the black panther again.

"Leave him to me," I said and shot down all the tin cans on the top of Joyce. This was too much for that sensitive soul who rose, pulled on his frayed trousers and shirt, took his ash plant with the handle at right angles to the shaft, and in silence left the tower forever. This will explain the rather obscure reference to the black panther in *Ulysses*. But I am sure that the scholiasts can explain it more obscurely.

Apparently he bore me no resentment. He may have thought that Trench had done the shooting, for he makes some comments on my visitor from Oxford. To this day I am sorry for that thoughtless horseplay on such a hyper-sensitive and difficult friend. But, if he had not pawned my rifle, he would have been less gun-shy. Trench fell in love with a titled Irish enthusiast and shot himself, being crossed in love.

In September, 1912, some years after Joyce walked out of the tower, I received in the mail from Flushing, Holland, a long strip of paper which looked like a galley proof and contained a poem of about one hundred lines. It was from Joyce, and was called "Gas From a Burner," obviously a reference to the burner in AE's Hermetic

Society room. Of all the self-revelations, "epiphanies," or portraits of the artists he ever wrote, this was the most revealing. It was all revolt, all bitterness.

In the poem, Joyce uses as his mouthpiece the manager of Maunsell's publishing firm. Maunsell's was the publisher who had printed Joyce's *Dubliners* and then burned all the copies but the one which Joyce took back with him to the continent. Maunsell's might have been one of the most successful publishers in Dublin had it not been in the hands of a man with a "traveling bag," that is a traveling salesman. Between literature and lingerie, the firm fell.

A passage from Joyce's letter to the press on his treatment by "Maunsell's manager" throws considerable light on the situation. Joyce had been asked by one of the firm's backers to submit his book, *Dubliners*. "I did so," he writes, "and after about a year, in July, 1909, Messrs. Maunsell signed a contract with me for publication of the book on or before the 1st of September, 1910. In December, 1909, Messrs. Maunsell's manager begged me to alter a passage in one of the stories, *Ivy Day in the Committee Room*, wherein some reference was made to Edward the VIIth. I agreed to do so much against my will, and altered one or two phrases. Messrs. Maunsell continually postponed the date of publication and, in the end, wrote asking me to omit the passage or change it radically. I declined to do either . . ."

Maunsell's manager had neither courage nor perspicacity. Had he had either he would have realized, as someone had evidently realized for him in Synge's case, that here was genius going begging for publication. Worse was to follow. The printer refused to hand over the copies and had the type distributed and the edition burned. This was enough to turn Joyce completely against the Irish literary movement, which he associated with Lady Gregory and her set.

To return to the poem; Maunsell's manager is speaking:

Ladies and gents, you are here assembled
To hear why earth and heaven trembled
Because of the black and sinister arts
Of an Irish writer in foreign parts.
He sent me a book ten years ago
I read it a hundred times or so,
Backwards and forwards, down and up,
Through both the ends of a telescope.
I printed it all to the very last word
But by the mercy of the Lord
The darkness of my mind was rent
And I saw the writer's foul intent.
But I owe a duty to Ireland:
I hold her honour in my hand,
This lovely land that always sent
Her writers and artists to banishment
And in a spirit of Irish fun
Betrayed her own leaders, one by one.
'Twas Irish humour, wet and dry
Flung quicklime into Parnell's eye;
... O Ireland my first and only love
Where Christ and Caesar are hand and glove!
O lovely land where the shamrock grows!
(Allow me, ladies, to blow my nose)
To show you for strictures I don't care a button

The choice of Dublin men and places as subjects for naturalism.

Here the sentiments are obviously out of character and the voice becomes that of Joyce, who has not won to his prerogative of speaking twice-tongued.

James Joyce: A Portrait of the Artist

I printed the poems of Mountainy Mutton
And a play he wrote (you've read it I'm sure)
Where they talk of "bastard," "bugger" and "whore."

A Mountainy Singer by Joseph Campbell.

And a play on the Word and Holy Paul
And some woman's legs that I can't recall
Written by Moore, a genuine gent
That lives on his property's ten per cent:
I printed mystical books in dozens:
I printed the table book of Cousins

One of AE's circle and a member of the Hermetic Society.

Though (asking your pardon) as for the verse
'Twould give you a heartburn on your arse:
I printed folklore from North and South
By Gregory of the Golden Mouth:

Lady Gregory.

I printed poets, sad, silly and solemn:
I printed Patrick What-do-you-Colm:
I printed the great John Milicent Synge
Who soars above on an angel's wing
In the playboy shift that he pinched as swag
From Maunsell's manager's traveling bag.
But I draw the line at that bloody fellow
That was over here dressed in Austrian yellow
Spouting Italian by the hour
To O'Leary Curtis and John Wyse Power
And writing of Dublin dirty and dear
In a way no blackamoor printer could bear

Obviously the speaker, who is Maunsell's manager, could not pillory himself thus. The word "shift" in Synge's *Playboy of the Western World* had caused a week of rioting of Puritanical ignoramuses in The Abbey Theatre some years previously, 1907. The shift is stolen from the traveling bag, for Maunsell's manager traveled in ladies' underwear.

**** *** *****! Do you think I'll print
The name of the Wellington Monument,
Sydney Parade and the Sandymount tram
Downes's cakeshop and Williams's jam?
I'm damned if I do—I'm damned to blazes!
Talk about *Irish Names of Places*

A famous book written by a namesake of Joyce.

It's a wonder to me upon my soul
He forgot to mention Curly's Hole.

A bathing pool at Dollymount Clontarf dangerous to non-swimmers.

No, ladies, my press shall have no share in
So gross a libel on Stepmother Erin.

The manager was an Ulster Scot so Erin is only his "stepmother."

· *60* ·

I pity the poor—that's why I took
A red-headed Scotchman to keep my book.
Poor sister Scotland, her doom is fell;
She cannot find any more Stuarts to sell.
My conscience is fine as Chinese silk:
My heart is as soft as buttermilk.
Colm can tell you I made a rebate
Of one hundred pounds on the estimate
I gave him for his Irish Review.
I love my country, by herrings I do!
I wish you could see what tears I weep
When I think of the emigrant train and ship.
That's why I publish far and wide
My quite illegible railway guide.
In the porch of my printing institute
The poor and deserving prostitute
Plays every night at catch-as-catch-can
With her tight-breeched British artilleryman
And the foreigner learns the gift of the gab
From the drunken, draggletail Dublin drab.
Who was it said, Resist not evil?
I'll burn that book, so help me devil.

. . . .

The manager himself!

This was written when there was a British garrison in Dublin. The double reference to the two breeches, of the trousers and the gun is characteristic.

Reference to treatment his own book got at the hands of Maunsell's!

Twelve years or so later, Joyce called on me in Ely Place. I shook the lank hand. He ignored the offer of a chair.

He stared about the room, then he looked out of the bay window and inspected the garden.

"Is this your revenge?" he inquired.

"Revenge on what?" I asked, puzzled.

"On the public."

And with that cryptic remark he left. I never saw that contrary man again.

Mr. Pirrie, Pyrophile

In A SIDE STREET BY THE
river the old houses leaned like gossips, wise in their generation, to converse with one another. They had an advantage over gossips wise in a generation, for they had seen many generations come, grow and go, stay and pass away, and had nodded as if to say, "Just so." But all through the centuries of their watchfulness they had never gazed down on such a sight as was to be seen now. They could not include this sight in their significant, "Just so."

Ringed with copper and shining brass, puffing smoke and steam, the newest of all fire engines stood, seething with power, on its bright red chassis outside one of the houses. There was no fire within; but the houses "belonged to the Ryans," the husband and father of whom was Mike Ryan, Captain of James's Gate Division of the Dublin Fire Brigade, for so the Fire Department is named in Dublin. Captain Mike Ryan's section included the eighty acres of the great Brewery of Guinness, and Stevens Hospital as well as the lunatic asylum called St.

Patrick's which was left to the nation by Dean Swift. South and east it was bounded by the river and Winetavern Street.

The Brigade had just disbanded after one of the processions that the Lord Mayor led through the city on St. Patrick's Day in the days when there were pageants and processions in Dublin. The Captain was at home eating a snack of lunch. Outside, the crowd gathered goggle-eyed. There were few men about, for they could not return from the procession as quickly or as promptly as the Brigade. It was doubtful if they would even if they could, for in those days Dublin was not depressed by the morality of the mediocre; and its taverns were not closed on St. Patrick's Day. So women and little children enjoyed a view at close quarters of the shining glory that brightened the drab street like the visit of a Prince. The awe that reigned was suddenly broken by the curses of an old woman who fell through a little boy's hoop. Her language might have sounded somewhat profane to the uninitiated, but it revealed an intimacy with the heavenly hierarchy that was comforting to the citizens of a country where religion entered into the every-day life of the people. It was not because it was a symbol of eternity that she drew the attention of Heaven to the hoop; but because it had become tangled in her legs. It was the hoop she cursed and not the little boy or her own curiosity; and this made her offense, if any, lighter, for her curse was directed, not at one of God's creatures, but at an inanimate thing. Her words were drowned in a general murmur, "Here's the Captain." But it was a less popular man, his brother-in-law, who appeared. His preparations for driving off on the engine made him less popular still. But presently, now that the steam was entering the cylinders, the Captain himself emerged, magnificent, a helmeted figure, tall and burly and belted with a great belt that carried an ax. His black leather boots went half way up his thighs and his dark blue uniform lined and faced with red could not hide the outlines of his chest and arms. Firemen wore brass helmets then and not the non-conducting black ones of today. High in front of the shining engine the brass-helmeted Brigade drove away. Cheers rose only to die in the suddenly darkened and deserted street. A few small boys tried to run after it, but they were soon out-distanced on the hilly street.

George Pirrie turned the corner. He thought he saw something glancing against the gray walls of Christ Church. He took out his latchkey and ascended the stairs so lately distinguished. He had yet to learn what he had missed.

George Pirrie occupied the top story of the house of the Ryans for fourteen years, from the days when he had to be up at five in the morning to check the casks as they left the Brewery on lorry or lighter for cross-channel ships or the cellars of the city, to the present time when, a man of authority and substance, he went to his office in the Brewery at the more human hour of eight o'clock.

George Pirrie was a little man, short and trim, but no one would think of him as a small man, for his connection with the Brewery gave him, if not height, status. Small men are either geniuses or eccentrics. No one thought of his size. They regarded only his position, for the Brewery, being a Protestant institution, emanated the respectability and authority of the Ascendancy. Each Brewer as he sat at his post felt this authority, for he was a product of Winchester and Balliol. He felt himself a *vates* as he sat at his vat brewing the best ale in the world, a brew that could bring quarrels, mirth or the prophetic phrensy, spiritual conditions these; to the material body it could bring health and strength—a food for invalids.

Mr. Pirrie had a small library off his living room on the top floor. It consisted mostly of books on fire-fighting with the histories of the development of modern apparatus; pictures of the lofty scaling ladders of the New York Fire Department with steering wheels fore and aft to direct them through the streets. He knew all there was to be known about fire brigades or departments from the first in the New World to the quaintest of them all, the Fire Brigade of Constantinople which the merchants of that city buy off if it threatens to extinguish a burning store and thus interfere with the will of Allah. Only Mr. Pirrie's lack of inches prevented him from being a fireman and not an official in a brewery. He was as closely associated with fire as he could well be. Did he not live with the family of a fire captain?

The Captain and his wife had seven children. Ellsie, the eldest, brought Mr. Pirrie his breakfast before she left for school. As he was absent during the day the noise of the youngsters did not disturb him. It was a pleasant arrangement. On Sundays there was always the possibility that the Captain would invite him down, when the chil-

dren had gone to bed, to join him in tasting the distilla-
tion of Bow Lane on the opposite bank of the river. Jame-
son's Distillery stood on the north bank of the Liffey and
looked at the great Brewery across that fortunate stream
from which, strange to say, neither distillery nor brewery
drew water, for they had wells of their own in the country
which were piped into the town.

The Captain was not an imaginative man, that is to
say, he was a bad historian. It took years before Mr.
Pirrie discovered that Captain Ryan had been to New
York, and when he did discover it, it took much question-
ing to get a clear picture of how they fought fire in that
great metropolis. Accounts in the receptions the Captain
attended and the speeches Captain Purcell, who led the
Delegation, made were substituted for what really interested Mr. Pirrie. "What do they do when one of their
skyscrapers goes on fire?" he asked.

"They don't," was all he got from Captain Ryan. Mr.
Pirrie was a mild little man. He did not like to press a
question.

"Strange," was all he said, and he said it like a sigh.

"Fire-proof," the Captain retorted.

So the evening would wear on: Mr. Pirrie avid for information; the Captain taking for granted what meant
Life and Adventure to Mr. Pirrie.

One evening he ventured to ask if it were true that the
fire-stations in New York had steel pillars down which
the firemen could slide to save time when answering an
alarm.

"Sure," said Captain Ryan.

No; there was not much to be got out of the Fire Captain. There was another disappointment that troubled Mr. Pirrie. The Captain was accustomed to sit at home after dinner in his stockinged feet. Gone was his uniform with its brazen helmet, his belted ax, and his thigh-high boots. It seemed a desecration. To the Captain it not only seemed but it was a relaxation from the weight of armor he had to carry while on duty.

"You were asking how we got on when the New York Fire Department invited us over to be their guests."

"I was interested," Mr. Pirrie affirmed.

"Well, them's the boys that can drive like blazes."

"Yes?" said Mr. Pirrie, his mind on tiptoe.

"I remember how we went to a place called the Antlers over a bridge miles long. We got there just in time. Them boys can drive."

"A fire?"

"No. A clam bake. They don't have things like that in this country. More's the pity. We went with bells ringing and sirens blowing enough to raise the dead. The Elks lent us the place.

"Talking of fires," the Captain continued as if making a concession to an amateur, "they have red cars that clear the way, and brass double hydrants, 'stand pipes' they call them, that can throw a jet ninety feet high."

But there was a far greater disappointment in store for Mr. Pirrie. At a fancy dress ball at Lord Iveagh's (his Lordship was head of the Brewery), Dr. Lumbsden, the doctor to the Brewery, had appeared dressed as a fireman. Where did he get the uniform? Captain Ryan lent it to him! Why had not Mr. Pirrie thought of that? And it was such a matter-of-fact gesture on the part of the Fire Captain that he did not even mention it when Mrs. Ryan was going through a list of the guests and the costumes they wore, until she came to Dr. Lumbsden. "Dr. Lumbsden, a Captain in the Dublin Fire Brigade."

Mr. Pirrie gave an exclamation.

"Show him the note of thanks," Mrs. Ryan requested.

"It's behind the clock." And Mrs. Ryan took it out and gave it to Mr. Pirrie.

"You are a bigger man than I," he read, "but it made things all the merrier when they saw me floundering on the dance floor in your boots."

Mr. Pirrie could have floundered just as well as Dr. Lumbsden; and floundered in the privacy of his apartment.

Columbus died on land, having been land-locked in jail. What irony there is in the fate of heroes! Some workmen were working down in a manhole twenty feet below the surface of the street. Their mates failed to get an answer when they signaled to them. One of them grew alarmed and reported to the police, who promptly called the Fire Brigade and dashed to the site of the accident. The Brigade reached the scene as soon as the police. "Gassed," announced the Fire Captain.

"I can't send men where I wouldn't go myself. Give me a line." So saying he lowered himself down by the staples that were fitted to the side of the shaft. A young constable followed. They never reached the surface alive again. Thus in the dark and in the cold far under the surface of the street died Mike Ryan, Fire Captain, fighting for his fellow man.

Tibet has nothing on Ireland when it comes to post-mortal observances. The wake of the Fire Captain lasted three days. Mr. Pirrie did not attend it. This was due not to a lack of respect for the dead but an undue respect for the living, which included himself and the Brewery. He knew that the young brewers who wore such fancy stockings would say that attending Irish wakes "was not done." That kept Mr. Pirrie away. But he had an overwhelming experience one morning. All the might of the Fire Brigade was drawn up before the house and down the adjoining streets. They were giving the gallant Fire Captain a public funeral. His coffin was carried on a great fire wagon draped with the city hall's flag. Before the catafalque and far behind it the armor of the Brigade filed on. Mr. Pirrie accompanied it for miles, walking as close as he could to the new fire engine. Never before had he appreciated the might of fire. Just as he had lost connection with the Brigade, as he thought, it turned out in full panoply to honor his friend. He felt drawn closer than ever to the dead man as he gazed sadly at the brass helmet and the ax laid upon the coffin lid. What would become of them?

Though he did not attend the wake, he was not remiss in offering his condolences to the widow. He did not dare to give notice that he intended to seek other quarters. Her loss was too recent to add another to it. But he felt that sooner or later it would appear unseemly to remain in the house of an unchaperoned lady. True, as he suggested to himself, the children were chaperons. What would the Brewery think?

Thoughts such as these were dispelled one evening when he was invited in "for a minute" as he ascended the stairs. Over the mantel piece hung the helmet and ax of the Captain. "With the compliments of the Brigade," he read. "I knew you'd like to see it," Mrs. Ryan remarked, referring to the complimentary note attached to the ax. Mr. Pirrie was thrilled. The helmet! And that ax had hewn down blazing walls! Doubtless it was the attraction of helmet and ax that brought Mr. Pirrie down when he came in the old days to talk with the Captain after the children had gone to bed. He found that he could get more information from Mrs. Ryan. Women have a way of seeing things as a series of images, which is more than can be said for men of action, including the late Captain.

Mr. Pirrie gazed at the mantel shelf. Mrs. Ryan followed his eye. She simpered as she said, "That's of him when we were married. Of course he had to give up waxing his mustache when he joined the Brigade." But it was of no amateurish photograph Mr. Pirrie was thinking. What was the history of the helmet and the ax? The dinge on the helmet?

"How did he get that dinge on the helmet?"

"Oh, that! He was fighting a fire" (how the expression thrilled Mr. Pirrie!), "fighting a fire up at St. Patrick's and one of the loonies threw something at him. Only for that helmet it might have broken his head or thrown him off the ladder. So he says to me."

Mr. Pirrie pondered for many days. On another occasion as the evening wore into night he ventured to inquire into the history of the ax. Mrs. Ryan knew little of its history.

"He used it for breaking down windows and doors, mostly at night when a fire breaks out and the people in the house are asleep in their beds. There's no time to ask for a key."

Mr. Pirrie pondered and came to the conclusion that it must be somewhat hard for Mrs. Ryan and her seven children to make ends meet on the pension of a Fire Captain. Yet it would be indelicate to offer her monetary assistance. His object could be reached just as well were he to buy for a substantial sum the helmet and the ax.

Mrs. Ryan had been out "shopping" for the greater part of the day. The strain had evidently told on her because she required a little "spirits" to assure sleep. Mr. Pirrie who joined in "well, just half a glass" thought the moment favorable.

"I have been thinking that it might go some way in educating the little ones as well as helping household expenses, if you were to sell and I were to buy that helmet and ax."

Though couched with due consideration, the effect of the speech on Mrs. Ryan was considerable. She extended her hand to arm's length toward Mr. Pirrie and shook with silent tears. She rose and stood by the fireplace. She raised her head and gazed at the helmet above.

She was not an uncomely figure. That is what occurred at the moment, in spite of his confusion, to Mr. Pirrie. With Ellsie fourteen and that photograph of Ryan with waxed mustaches, Mrs. Ryan need not be more than in her middle thirties.

She turned from gazing and wiped her eyes.

"It's all I have," she said, a mother forgetful.

Mr. Pirrie was infected by the spirit of sympathy. He had a vision as he gazed at her swimming eyes and at the arms above her head. He saw far beyond the Fire Brigade and the streets of Dublin, far away over the ocean to the Fire Department of New York. He saw the scarlet fire engines and the Fire Chief's red cars, bells, and sirens! The roar and diapason on the way to a fire. Even if the skyscrapers did not catch fire, there were other buildings, maybe, just as high that did. He saw himself high in mid-air. The helmet would save his eyes as he smashed a window. "Jets ninety feet high!" He heard the Fire Captain's voice. He also heard his widow's voice, and in the flesh.

"It's all I have. Don't ask me to sell it."

"But . . . but . . . I did not mean to be unkind. I meant that if I had it, it would not be far away."

"Far away?" Mrs. Ryan looked over her handkerchief. Her tear-bright eyes pleaded for elucidation.

"Do you mean you would marry me, George?" she murmured. George Pirrie rose to the occasion for the house seemed all on fire. He had to assume that helmet and that ax.

"I do, indeed," he said.

Missed by a Mark

Christmas AND WAR ARE two ideas very much opposed and yet they combined in a remarkable way to influence the career of John Ethelred Bateman, as this tale will disclose if the reader have the patience to peruse it.

John Ethelred Bateman was of Cromwellian descent, that is, he came of a family of Planters who had benefitted or suffered (it depends on the commentator) by becoming "more Irish than the Irish themselves." On his father's death his uncle became the owner of Ballymacoda House. Now his uncle was dead and the property was entailed for him subject to a life interest for his mother.

The news of his uncle's death reached Ethelred, or, since that was too much of a name for the irreverent lips of medical students, "Red" Bateman as he sat in his rooms overlooking the pleasant sward of Provost's Garden in Trinity College, Dublin. He was in the middle of the second half of his medical examinations, which meant that he had been a student for more than three years and that, if he passed the second half, he would have only two more examinations, the Finals in Surgery and Medicine, to pass before becoming a doctor qualified to practise anywhere in the United Kingdom, and that is everywhere there are complaisant people.

He was a brilliant student, an Honor man, and, though the news upset him, he continued to sit for two days until the last paper was finished and handed in. There could be no doubt of the result for, from his uncle down to the most envious "medical," there was no one who had any want of appreciation of his talents.

When he arrived at Ballymacoda House, he was in time for only one day of the wake; but, if we may judge by the appearances of some of the mourners—and we all know that such judgements may be fallacious—he was in time enough. When the townspeople and the neighbors had taken their fill of grief and his uncle had been laid to rest in the well-kept cemetery under the square tower of the Protestant Church, the chief mourners, among whom was included *ex officio* the family lawyer, returned to the house for a ceremony that sometimes brings consolation to the widow and the orphan, the reading of the will. Beddy, the attorney with the big head and eyes that might be taken as watering from grief or its antidote, proceeded to read the will in a husky voice that was as equivocal as his look was deceptive. It was meant to be as impersonal as the Law itself, but something ineffable bubbled up and made it quaver. It might have been solicitude for future business with the family or the effects of the wake.

"To my beloved nephew, John Ethelred, the sum of

£400 a year free of all charges or incumbrances while he is engaged in his examinations, the yearly payments to cease absolutely when he becomes a Doctor of Medicine."

Now £400 is $2,000 which goes a long way with an unmarried man in Ireland, England, Scotland, and Wales where there are millions of men married and with families living on less. Mrs. Bateman was to hold the house during her lifetime, an arrangement which was well suited to the circumstances because it left John free to pursue his studies under the terms of his uncle's will.

The country people were very sympathetic and reminiscent. John was amazed by the help they had rendered and by the amount for which he was beholden to them while he was still in his perambulator. He had only to call and they would render every kind of unnecessary service in the future. It was enough to make a superficial observer think that it took a death to bring out the best points of an Irishman.

At last the funeral guests had departed and John was left to talk to his mother and plan for the future. It was comforting to know that he would not be a charge on her during the expensive years of studentship. So well had he been provided for that there was a possibility of a surplus which might be hidden away against the time when it would be necessary to set up in practice. Or it might contribute to the upkeep of the House which, like all such houses in Ireland, had "a back door" out of which went many leakages of soap, candles, flour and tea, leakages that bore an uncanny relationship to the resources of the House and the tolerance of its owner.

As the train bore John along through the golden bogs of the midlands he could see here and there, like rocks in the expanse of purple heather, the neglected butts that some departed landlord had built for his guests at some long forgotten "shoot." Far away to the south the horizon was fretted by long thin lines of spruce and fir.

The cushions of the first class carriage were comfortable. He let his head fall back on the lace cover of the chair. His mind revolved confusedly the crowded experiences of the past week. His mind's eye could see Diamond, the gombeen man, that is the dominant shop-keeper of the village, who had everyone on his books (and no discharge possible), with his otter-skin waistcoat showing above his black Sunday coat as he took his turn with the bearers of his uncle's coffin. He recalled the sudden silence and the expressions of grief that overlaid the laughing card players in the kitchen when he entered to see if they were well supplied with whiskey and tobacco. Billy the Butler, self-styled because he polished the silver and the fire irons, though he never entered the dining room when the family were seated, came clearly before him mumbling, "I heard a flutter," as if he were the only one worthy of an apparition. Again he saw the long bright blade of Nick the Loy's one-sided loy or shovel as it dug heartily into the soil of his uncle's grave. The sense of expectancy and agitation of the household he felt again and the confusion caused by death. Regret for his uncle, for the man who had called him his "beloved nephew" assailed him now in the peace of the carriage as it could not in the distraction of the house. The twenty-bore with the right barrel open for snipe that his uncle had given him on his twelfth birthday; he had it still. It was placed in the gun room with the pair of Purdeys which came to him with other gear now that he was heir to all his uncle's "effects." The old man's pride in his race, a pride that unconsciously separated him from the "people," had little influence on him. Perhaps he should be less democratic now that he was a man of property. If a man is to retain any vestige of property in Ireland, he must remain aloof. Aloofness for a medical student is something hard to come by. Then there was his uncle's attitude to work, servile work. He considered that an insufferable pollution.

Now that the funeral was over he felt a sense of relief. He felt disloyal to his uncle's memory to feel relief that he was dead and buried. No; the relief he felt was at having escaped from all the hurly-burly connected with the death. He heard his name called and abruptly he realised that the telegram was for him. He had passed with honors. There remained only two more examinations and he would be a qualified professional man. Two more examinations —six months—and he would be without an income. To pass his Finals meant the loss of a small fortune. True, he might make much more than four hundred pounds a year at his profession; but that would mean that he would have, first of all, to wait, and all the time to work. Work. He might join one of the Services, but that meant more work. It meant that he would be subordinated to discipline. Even the pension at the end of his life would hardly exceed the sum he already possessed. He turned over the terms of his uncle's will in his mind. Could that darkly

humorous man have hinted that he would be a fool to go
on with his examinations? He knew that Glendenning, the
village doctor, did not impress his uncle much. "To cease
absolutely." There was almost a threat conveyed in that,
or a hint that there was no need to become qualified, to
pass. His uncle wanted someone to inherit Ballymacoda
House who would live the life of a country gentleman as
he had lived it; and how could you do that while practis-
ing medicine? If it were someone else's will he were inter-
preting, he would have been disinterested and have read
the intimation as it was apparently meant to be read. His
uncle's will meant that he was to enjoy four hundred a
year for life and to return to Ballymacoda whenever he
could. His uncle might have been ashamed to allow the
neighbours to know that he had only four hundred a year
to leave so he concealed it with this condition. He saw it
all clearly now. He must fail in his examinations for the
rest of his life and yet continue with the pretext of study-
ing. A "chronic" medical! What a career. And yet that
was what the will conveyed. He began to feel less grateful
to his uncle for putting such a condition into his will.

He reached his rooms above the Provost's Garden with
the problem unsolved. Another problem presented itself.
If he were to fail deliberately in his examinations under
the terms of his uncle's will it would be necessary to sit for
them now and again. But how could an Honor student
dishonor himself by failure before examiners who, knowing his record, were friendly disposed towards him and
almost cordial? He resolved that one more examination
was all he could take in Trinity College. When he failed

in that, he hoped that his failure would be attributed to the effect of his uncle's death. If they came to that conclusion, there would be more truth in it than they could suspect.

With his change of plans came a change of character. He ceased to be a studious recluse. When the time allowed for residence in College expired, he took rooms in Pleasants Street which enters Heytesbury Street at right angles. Heytesbury Street was quite close to the Meath Hospital. Medical students of the wilder sort lived there. The poorer ones drank in Kennedy's at the corner of the South Circular Road. Those of the better class, and a Trinity man was always of the better class, drank in Mooney's in Harry Street where the more deserving became acquainted with Nosey Coote. Nosey Coote cottoned at once to Jack Bateman, for he was a scion of the landlord class and recognized an equal in his new acquaintance. They had one thing in common. They were both "pensioners." Bateman had a pension for as long as he was sitting for examinations and Nosey had a pension for so long as he kept away from the family estates in County Monaghan. Nosey Coote was particular in his friendships. He refused to know Bird Flanagan who lacked a background comparable to his. There was an air of lost distinction about Nosey Coote.

After some months, one day in the cosey, that is, in a small reserved space at the end of the bar into which only the bartender can see, Jack Bateman revealed his position to Nosey Coote. Nosey sat in his accustomed seat where the marble met the mahogany. He propped himself against the wall in his corner and in silence heard the tale. He saw nothing wrong in the situation. He himself, as he in turn confided, lived a dammed conditional existence. He saw nothing wrong with sitting for examinations provided they did not occur too frequently in the year. "Would once a year be enough? Why, man, that's excellent. You are free to move around. I cannot go home."

"I have to keep on the books of some medical school, otherwise I shall cease to be a medical student. And once the lawyers get to raising legal questions there will be no money left at all."

"There are dozens of colleges, enough to last a lifetime," said Nosey Coote.

"I am joining the College of Surgeons next week. That may give me more exams. to sit for. There were only two to go in Trinity College and I am afraid I missed one. When they kick me out after five or six years from 'The Surgeons,' I can go to Edinburgh where all the 'chronics' from Dublin go."

The news of John Ethelred Bateman's failure in the Final Examination in Medicine caused considerable consternation. Apparently no one was more surprised than the victim who, to save his face somewhat, went about confiding in the better known gossips that he had "missed by a mark." After that he took his name off the books and joined, as he announced to Nosey Coote, The Royal College of Surgeons.

Fair and softly the years passed by. John spent his summers in Ballymacoda and his winters in Mooney's in Harry Street. But, alas, there is nothing stable in this world of flux. The Board of the College of Surgeons decided that there was a limit even to missing by a mark. So John left for Edinburgh. After a few weeks spent "swinging to adjust compasses" in his new latitude, John settled down with the Scots who being Gaels get on well with the Irish and more than well with those who happened to be more Irish than the Irish. Here they found nothing reprehensible in his failures. When a man is in a position to stand drinks all round to drown his disappointment, the more failures the better and "Lang life tae ye." So drank the Scots.

The lady medicals attributed his failures to their own charms. So all went on smoothly until the year 1940, until the Michelmas Examinations to be exact. Medical students were not drafted into the Navy or the Army. They were left to pursue their studies and they studied all the harder lest it appear that by failing they were shirking war. John E. Bateman's reputation as a chronic was so well established however, that such an imputation could never cling to his name even if he missed by more than a mark. He had long ago ceased to have misgivings about examinations. He presented himself without a qualm. The familiar round began. Each student sat at a separate desk and amid silence an attendant dealt out the examinations papers. The examiners patrolled the hall to see that no communications passed between students and that no notes were used.

After a few moments' scrutiny of the papers a rustle of relief or a sigh of disappointment could be heard in the hall and then the writing began.

Nonchalantly John stared at his paper. He had no misgivings. Listlessly he read.

"You are required to answer seven of the ten questions set." Therefore it would be safe to answer six. Almost all the questions dealt with traumatic injuries, a reminder that a war was on.

> In its course through the right brachial plexus a
> bullet severs the thoracodorsalis nerve; enumerate
> the muscles of the back that will be paralyzed.

John spotted the trap. Else why if there were no trap should the examiner have telegraphed "the muscles of the back." The examiner had almost told you the answer. There was a trap somewhere. Very well, thought John, if I answer this easy one the less credit I will get, so he wrote in his neat writing, "*Latissimus dorsi.*"

Another paralytic question was the next. It is the facial nerve that is severed this time.

That would leave half the face flaccid. The eye could not close fully because the lower lid could not move up. The food would fall away from the teeth and into the helpless cheek. The side of the nose—the face of his friend Coote came before his mind's eye and he smiled. About a baker's dozen of muscles were involved in this paralysis. He smiled again. It was only last night that he went over them with a little brush on the face of a lady student who wondered what muscles went to a smile. He wound up with "*Levator anguli oris.*" There was little risk in letting them have the lot.

However, "the best laid schemes of mice and men gang aft aglee."

The Examiners, in answer to an appeal from the War Office, had reduced the standard from 75% to 50% overnight. John E. Bateman nevertheless was short by one mark. It was conceded.

About ten days later as he entered Poosie's he was greeted with a cheer. The taller of the lady medicals permitted herself to kiss him on the cheek where the *levator anguli oris* operates. The barmaid shook his hand with both of hers. The "chronics" appeared to be transfigured. He smiled inquiringly.

"What's all this about?"

"Didn't you read the results? We are all through. You did pretty well yourself. The drinks are on the house."

"What?" he asked in consternation. "Do you mean to tell me that I am a doctor?"

"We're all qualified," Angus said. "And commissions coming." Angus was the doyen of the chronics. He had been in Edinburgh for ten years.

"They must be damned hard up for doctors when they passed me," John said humbly. "I could answer only six questions. I feared that I had missed."

"It would be just the same if you had sent in a blank. They are awfully short of doctors at the front, and even the Americans cannot supply them," the tall lady said and she seemed to know.

Angus broke into broad Scotch. "There's anither thing. It's getting close tae Christmas noo. Aiblins the thoct of it saftened thae examiners' dour hairts." Then he sang,

"We are no fou, we are no fou;
But just a drappie in our ee.
The cock may craw, the day may daw;
But aye we'll taste the barley bree."

John's farewell to Edinburgh was very sad. But what
a welcome he got at Ballymacoda. His despondency was
attributed to the rigors of the long journey. His train
pulled in just as darkness was falling. Darkness would
not matter: it was all the better for the bonfires and the
torchlight procession.

His foot had hardly touched the platform when the
stationmaster took him aside and asked anxiously, "How
am I doing, Doc?"

Outside he could hear the appreciations of the crowd
telling each other in voices meant for him to hear of his
trials and his attributes. "Away for fourteen years."
"Sure. He took the long course." "He knows more than
most."

He was lifted shoulder high and borne to a six-roomed
house known as the Grand Hotel. Supper was set in the
dining room upstairs. But before supper, there was a little
ceremony. He was presented with a shingle that was illu-
minated with wolf hounds, twisted lines, and a Celtic
cross. Dr. Glendenning, who was chairman of the Reception Committee, presented the shingle, which was taste-
fully (as the newspapers had it next morning) decorated
by both Sister Monica and the Rector's wife, thus showing how all denominations joined in welcoming Ballymacoda's distinguished son.

The cheers were becoming uproarious outside the Grand

Hotel. To calm them, Ballymacoda's distinguished son ordered a few firkins of Guinness to be broached and sent to those who were attending the bonfire in the Mall. This gave those at supper about half an hour's respite.

Beddy sat near the hero. When he got a chance, the hero lamented his unfortunate success. "Don't let that worry you. You need never take the M.D. degree. And the will says, Doctor of Medicine. If you were in the U.S.A., where no one is allowed to practise unless he holds that degree, it would be different. Over here it is all right. It is an ornament not a necessity."

He wrung the little attorney's hand. Oh, what a relief! He kept his nose so deep in his glass that for all the world he looked for a moment like Nosey Coote.

Dr. Glendenning rose to speak. Somebody shouted, "Silence," but what sort of silence could he expect. The firkins had finished their work and the ambrosial night was being made raucous again. Cries of "Speech! Speech!" reached the dining room, and the shutters on the street level began to shake from the pressure outside. The Committee decided that the only thing to do was not to rouse the anger of the crowd by monopolizing the successful scientist and holding him in a hotel when all the town and country wanted a share in his glory. He would have to appear on the balcony and deliver the speech that they were demanding with increasing indignation. The crowd roared their appreciation when the window was raised to permit John Ethelred to appear on the balcony. He stooped under the window, reached the balcony, straightened himself up and began to speak. He could not be heard, so deafening were the cheers, which goes to show that it is not the content but the intention of a speech that matters in Ballymacoda. At last a deep silence fell upon the mob. They realised that they were missing something. The faces glowing from the torches gazed upwards at the first floor window of the Grand Hotel. The tall figure silhouetted against the window raised its arm. Every word was distinct:

"Fellow townsmen."

Cheers and cheers again and again. The speaker had to start afresh. He was grateful for any interruptions that would consume the time of his ordeal as an orator.

"Fellow townsmen!"

He began again. "Fellow townsmen and neighbours of Ballymacoda."

Again they roared applause.

"Fellow townsmen and men and women of Ballymacoda. I am so moved by your reception that I can only thank you in the words of the great Latin poet:

"Latissimus dorsi et levator anguli oris."

The cheering did not die away until he entered his home a mile from the Grand Hotel.

He Found the Spring

$\mathscr{Our}$ WELL WENT DRY LAST August in Vermont. The first time in sixty years, the landlady said. For my part, and I was only a visitor, I asked myself: Why should the water disappear when I appeared? I began to think that there might be some sinister connection between me and the dried-up well. The landlady, who was very practical, borrowed large milk tins and had them filled at a neighbor's house and poured them into the cistern in her house. This did not extend to my premises which were made out of a converted barn. No water for three weeks! Luckily the house stood over a brook and the brook had soap bubbles added to its own, morning and evening. I hated to defile that crystal clear and merry stream, although it was to blame to some extent because it had carried off the subsurface water that had made the house habitable for sixty years. It was beginning to be uninhabitable now. You have no idea how dependent civilization is upon a well. Wells have decided the sites of towns, villages, houses, and those "inhabited places" of which you read in war dispatches. I don't know what they are; but I know that they could not be inhabited at all if there were no water.

The landlady became more and more conscientious as the drought increased. I can find no more connection between conscience and the lack of water than between its disappearance and my arrival. Water drinkers are sometimes conscientious people; but in this instance, that would not be an explanation. The fact remains that she became so conscientious that she decided to sink an artesian well—for the lady guests, whose presence may have been accountable for her conscientiousness.

Now an artesian well is one that taps the deeper reservoirs of ground water. In spite of the misnomer, an artesian well in Vermont is any well that costs money to sink. Our landlady calculated that an artesian well would cost six hundred dollars at five dollars a foot (starting in the cellar where the surface was lowest) but if water could be found on the slope where the dried-up well was, the cost would be less than half; and the old pipe line would be available. She was as hardheaded as a nail and when she sent for a water diviner, I was thrilled with interest. I forgave her for being conscientious only for the ladies. I was glad that the well had gone dry, for I wanted to see a water diviner at work. I knew the disapproval with which such matters as the mild magic of water-finding were dismissed by "scientists," jealous because there were things in heaven and earth not dreamt of in their philosophy. I wanted to see something done that admitted of no explanation. I wanted badly to see something that would burst up the scientific and mechanical theories to which all the wonder and magic of the world have been reduced in this factual age of ours. I wanted the wonder and mystery of the time when all the world was young, restored. And the fact that such a shrewd business brain as our landlady's believed in the "dowser," or water diviner, was an assurance that I would see wonders at work.

He came in the car that was sent for him, a little gray man over seventy who was too small for his suit. He had gold-rimmed glasses and a graying mustache as thick as Rudyard Kipling's—who had been, too, at one time, a resident of Vermont. He carried a large flat brown paper bag. I was put beside him in the back of the car. Off we went to find the longed-for spring. On the way he discussed his health and said not a word about his mission. He seemed as assured as a surgeon who is driving to an operation with a mind free from anxiety because of self-confidence and a mastery of his craft. For two years he had been suffering. He had lost weight. Couldn't I see that? Doctors, the ordinary doctors, were consulted without satisfactory results. How could scientists satisfy a magician? I found myself thinking. I had hit the nail. Evidently he believed in men of his own kind, inexplicable men with a natural endowment; for the only man who could cure him happened to be out in Rhode Island. He was persuaded to consult him. (I had brought all this on myself, all through sympathy, so share the results with me.) He did consult him. But here he takes on the tale.

"When I arrived, the dooryard was half-full of automobiles from all over the States. I was taken in earlier than I expected. 'Sit in that chair. It is my lucky chair,' said he. 'What countryman may you be?' I asked him. 'Well,' he said, 'if a countryman at all, I'm a full-blooded Indian and I got this gift from my mother and her mother before her and back and back.' So I sits down. 'Is it necessary to tell you my history and my trouble?' I asked him. He shook his head. 'Sit straighter,' he said. Then he held his hand an inch or two in front of my chest. 'It's not here,' said he."

"Did he touch you?" I asked. But he merely shook his head impatiently and went on with the story.

"Next he moved his hands down my thighs and legs, a couple of times. 'Do you feel anything?' he asked. 'I feel water flowing down my pants.' 'You guessed wrong. That's not water, that's blood,' said he. 'Your circulation has been out of order because your heart was not equal to it. . . .' "

I must have missed some of the narrative for with my usual annoying habit of letting associations distract and absorb me, I couldn't help being amused at the characteristic guess of the water diviner.

" 'Take a little tartar night and morning every Tuesday and Friday and you'll be all right,' he said. 'Do I owe you anything?' He shook his head. 'I am not allowed to take it; but you may make me a present if you wish.' "

"Are you all right?" I couldn't help asking. But the car was turning into a field and rocking. He took up the brown paper bag and as I was out first he gave it to me. The others gathered round him. He took out a thin, forked dry spray about twenty inches long on each limb with a little handle about three inches long.

"Guess what wood that is."

"Willow." "Ash." "Locust." They all guessed wrong. "Hazel," I said, and I was right, but he did not hear me and released the information with the added word "witch": witch hazel. I tried to get credit for my guess, but instead I got the wand to hold and that was all sufficing.

While they were going in the direction of the old well, I held the divining rod. I examined its dry and brittle condition. I let my mind wander back to the days when there must have been some sort of an understanding, a communion between what we are pleased to call inanimate things, such as rocks, streams, and trees, and mankind. Before this, union of man, beast, and tree was broken by the Tree of Knowledge, which is the hardheaded, dreamless, and mechanistic science of our time. And here was this gift, this sympathy with external Nature residing, as a remnant only, in a little unsophisticated man over seventy years of age—this understanding from the paradisal time!

From me whom he had appointed as his squire, he took the rod, the rod that is as immemorial as the wand of Mercury which you see to this day in the badge of the Army Medical Corps, or the Golden Arrow of the Hesperides.

He took the rod and, holding it in his hands with his thumbs turned out, he raised it up with the handle under his chin but not touching it. He took a great puff of breath, and swelling out his chest and thin cheeks, advanced, stepping high with a kind of solemn march, toward the dried-up well. When he was about two yards from it the wand began to quiver. We could see his hollow cheeks working behind his full mustache. He gathered himself and took a firmer hold of the wand. His knuckles grew white as he tightened his grip. Frantically the wand began to struggle and dip. He held on until his arms began to shake, too. Down the forked wand went until the handle pointed directly into the ground. Still he tried to hold it back. The right-hand side twig snapped in his hand. He regained his breath. "There's water there." And he pointed down and stood still until someone should mark the spot.

Now the landlady piped up. "Can you tell me how many feet down it is?"

(After all it was she who was paying for the exhibition, and the sinking of the new well.)

He chose another rod. Again he repeated the procedure with decreasing vehemence in his bearing. Ten times the rod dipped down, growing weaker and weaker with each inclination.

"Between nine and a half and ten feet," the sage announced. Then, his solemn ritual over, he relaxed and invited us all to try. I went first. Had I not carried the bag? I tried to throw my mind out of this trumpery coil of things and back to the days when men and gods mixed and walked the earth.

"After all," I said to myself, "you are perhaps the one person left who, though trained as a scientist, does not believe in science as an explanation of a way of life." Not a thing happened either to me or to the wand. Everyone tried. No results. In a way I was glad. I would hate to see the gift made common property. There was no fear of that, however. I could tell that by the assurance of the little man.

The check was made out for ten dollars. That was his fee and not a charge, as it might seem, of a dollar a foot. No—leave that to the drilling companies who believe in diamond-faced drills and not wands of witch hazel.

George H. Harris must have Scots' blood, I thought, when I heard him call out his name to the landlady who was filling in the check. That's what makes him fey or supernaturally gifted. He asked me how it came that I could tell. There was no use pretending that I had any gift for divination after my failure by the well. So I said that Harris was an island in the north of Scotland and that his was a well-known Scottish name. With that, he left for his home in Newfane.

I could not get over my utter failure to throw myself into a receptive mood for divining. I have plenty of sympathy with nature, but it did me little good. I, who am unhappy and incomplete when away from brooks and streams, was shut out from their confidence.

The next day the excavations for a new well were commenced. After they had gone down what I took to be ten but was only eight feet, and no water appeared, I was downcast. I was backing intuition against rules and regulations. But on the second day they struck what was probably the old flow that had been diverted by a fall of stone or clay; and it yielded thirty gallons an hour. The house required only three hundred gallons per day. I thought that it would be a kindly act to bring the diviner the good news.

He was sitting on his porch when I arrived.

"Water was found!" I shouted. But there must have been a hint of unseemly surprise in my voice. He came over to the car and had a long chat with the landlady about ways and means for lining the new well. When he had finished he turned to me and took me up where I had left off when I announced the good news.

"There's some that don't believe it," he said, with the assurance of a churchman who can afford to pity and to tolerate heretics.

The Hero in Man

At nightfall THE RAIN ceased. There was still a primrose wash with a few stars overhead behind the hills.

"It should be about here," the driver of the sidecar said as he pulled up. "This is the last boreen to the right before the top of the hill."

Cumbersomely, a great figure of a man descended. He was covered by a thin raincoat darkened on one side by the recent rain. He felt for the step with his foot. When he reached the ground, he fumbled in his pocket and, with beard sunk in his chest, looked over his spectacles to count his money with blue and childlike eyes. The driver went ahead to turn his horse a little way up the steep road. He thanked his passenger as he took his fare.

"That should be about right?"

"Indeed it is. God bless you, sir. If you like, I'll wait until the gossoon comes. He should be here any minute now."

"No, no," the passenger answered with the unintentional abruptness of the preoccupied. "If need be, I'll walk over the hill."

Slowly man and horse went down the road. The one lamp of the sidecar flickered on the lichen-dappled stones of the fence. It was soon hidden by the horizontal branches of a wind-swept tree.

The man in raincoat stood alone on the mountain side. The evening star was still high and small in the West. He gazed at it until its rays grew mellow.

Quietly out of the darkness a small hand took hold of his. It might have been the little hand of a leprechaun or one of the Good People who come out about this time of night to hold their hosting on the hills. He looked down and discerned the large eyes and pointed chin of a little boy. You would think from the matter of fact way that the big man took the little hand that he was familiar with the fairies, as indeed he was. With sure feet the boy led him along the spongy track. Whenever a bog hole full of stars lay in their path, "No, no, sir. Sideways, sideways!" the little boy would exclaim and lean against his companion to steer him in the dark.

"What's your name, little man?"

"Fahy, sir."

"How many brothers and sisters have you?"

"Six, sir. I'm the eldest, that's why Father sent me to meet you in the boreen when you said that you wanted to spare the horse. Sideways, sir, sideways."

"Is the meeting assembled?"

"What is it?"

"Are there many men with your father?"

"About a score, sir. Mr. Denroche hasn't come."

They floundered on till at length level beams that

seemed intensely bright flooded the dark moor. The lights
appeared to come from some long, low building or from
the ground floor of some large house. The lights flickered
as figures passed in front of them, to and fro.

"There's the meeting!" The little boy pulled at his
companion's hand. In response, the big man hastened his
steps not forgetting the fact that in Ireland one cannot
be unpunctual for a meeting of any kind.

In spite of the unusual approach, this was not one of
those "secret meetings" that are forbidden by law and
that consequently are popular and eagerly attended
throughout the country. It was the second and rather
listless meeting of the local Coöperative Society which the
big man, who was the Organizer from the city, was on his
way to address. The long, low building was the "Town
Hall" which a local squire had presented to the straggling
hamlet of a dozen houses to commemorate his son who
fell in France. The Coöperative movement was started
and supported by an aristocrat of Norman descent who
longed to devote himself to a "National Purpose" and
thought that to organize them for coöperation was the
best way of helping the people who were sorely in need
of help. Help from themselves; help from apathy, hope-
lessness, prejudice, cynicism, and suspicion which made
progress impossible and kept them at a dead end. Help
from themselves! The gombeen man was one of themselves. The gombeen man, chief storekeeper of the village
and the native magnate, was one of themselves, and he
held them all well down in his debt. All the villagers and
all the small-holders in the parish were in his books for

flour, tea, sugar, soap, fertilizers, cement. He could charge them what he liked and take it out of them in the price of commodities at compound interest. The only way you could extricate yourself was by a single cash payment. And who could make a cash payment with the markets as they were and the price of cattle at the mercy of the cattle-dealers? It wasn't as if you could hold out for a better price. Farm produce is perishable; and if you try to keep a calf, you won't have the wherewithal to fatten it —you have to let it go for what you can get. Without credit you would starve. You couldn't leave the gombeen man. There was nowhere else to go.

Wait. Yes, there was or, rather, there soon would be. There would be a coöperative bank from which the members could draw money at a nominal rate—or none at all —against the products of their industry.

The Organizer had arrived in time for the second meeting of the Coöperative Society in the mountain village of Cloona.

He faced the lamplight and took off his glasses which were still wet. As he polished them he began to speak. He spoke diffidently. In fact, he was a poor speaker until his soul was stirred about some injustice or in support of some ideal. He helped himself to begin by repeating one of his set speeches:

"In a country like this which is divided into so many small holdings, it is wasteful for a farmer to work by himself. If he works by himself, he must borrow by himself. He must sell by himself and make his purchases by himself and be forced to pay any price the retailer likes to charge. You all know that there is only one retailer in each village, and no man alone can get out of his clutches. He has got rich on what? On *you*. The banks have got rich on *you*. On each one of you separately. But they cannot bleed or exploit you if you are combined. Be your own bankers, your own salesmen, and your own buyers by joining this Society to the other Coöperative Societies in the country." He ceased and looked about him.

"Has anyone got a list of the members?" There was an awkward pause. A tall, middle-aged man, who had evidently been drilled, stood in the doorway, half out and half in. The audience felt as if their clothes had dried on them. The Organizer sensed the embarrassment. In some confusion he stammered, "Is there no list of members since the first meeting?"

He was not aware that there had been, since he founded the Society months ago, many meetings at the hearths of the neighbors. With the conservatism and the intuition and the sagacity of peasants, they had discussed the proposed society from a premise of suspicion. These are the questions they asked each other, and they were, as usual in such societies, personal: Who was the Organizer, anyway, to talk to them about farming? He wasn't a farmer. He couldn't tell you the difference between a springer and a calf. What would a farmer be doing with an easel, painting bog holes half the night and spending the rest of it lying up on the old rath where no decent Christian had any call to be? Passing that, suppose they did coöperate and establish a bank, where would your privacy be? Your account would be open to the wide world. If they all combined to sell together, who would do the selling for them and the buying—Denroche, the ex-sergeant? He might be a spy for all they knew. Once a policeman, always a policeman. And, finally, there arose in each man's mind the fear of losing some of his personality, his power of bargaining. All the fun would be taken out of the fair where neighbors met and toasted each other with the luck pennies when they sold a foal or a calf.

The silence continued. At last one of the audience, after a glance at the figure in the doorway, spoke as if he grudged meaning to his words.

"Well, sir, bad as it is, we think we'll go along in the old way."

Fasting, travel-weary, and wet as he was, the soul of the Organizer took fire. This was one of the dragons worthy of his spear: the dragon of apathy and suspicion that lurked in the soul of man. To fight such a reptile as this he had sacrificed wealth and position, for he believed that, hidden under cover of ignoble things, there was a nobility in the meanest of human beings; he believed that their present downfall was the result of some too weighty heroic labor undertaken by the human spirit; that it was this consecration of past purpose that played with such a tender light of night and the half light about their ruined lives. All the more pathetic was it because this nobleness was unknown to the fallen, and the heroic cause of so much pain was forgotten in life's prison house. He would devote himself to set free the Hero that he believed was in the soul of every man. He would appeal to them to strike off its shackles and set the dungeoned

Hero free. He seemed to increase in stature as he leaned forward.

"You will go on in the old way? But you are not going on in any way. You are stagnating. You are helpless and hopeless. Even a miserable and mean creature like the local usurer, the gombeen man, can strike fear into you and hold you down. You have lost your faith." He felt an antipathy rise among them at this, for "faith" to them had but one meaning. He hastened to explain. "I do not mean your religious faith but the faith on which that and everything else depends: your faith in yourselves. You are sunk so low and are so brow-beaten that you are not only willing to accept defeat, but to glory in it like the ballad-ist who made a song out of its disgrace: 'Oh, Shaun O'Dwyer na Glanna, we're worsted in the game.'

"How can you hope to rise beyond wretchedness if you have not unbounded hope and confidence in what your humanity, your country can do? If you do not believe in yourselves, do not make the world sick by protesting that you love your country and that you have a right to be free. What right have you to be free when you hug your chains? What right have you to associate with free men when you have condemned yourselves to the dungeons of suspicion? What right have you to be free as long as you find satisfaction in taking a beating like a dog lying down. Have confidence in yourselves!" He saw resentment arising in the dark faces. Their spirit was awakening. The Hero was stirring in man. He continued. He would enlist their rage in their own behalf.

"You are fine upstanding men all of you. Stand up to

the gombeen man not only here but all over the land. You
have seen American tourists here. You may have thought
that they were boastful. Well, let me tell you that, whatever their boasts may have been, they were, in all probability, understatements. I have been in the United States.
Its citizens cannot boast too much. What you call boast-
ing is only their expression of their self-confidence, that
self-confidence which has made a great civilization and
will continue to make it because each American believes
heart and soul in the future of his country and in the
powers of the American people. What Walt Whitman
called their 'barbaric yawp' may yet turn into the lordliest
speech and thought. But without self-confidence a race
will go no whither. If the Irish people do not believe they
can surpass the stature of any humanity which has been
upon the globe, then they had better all emigrate and
become servants to some superior race, or leave Ireland
to new settlers who may come here with the same high
hopes as the Pilgrim Fathers had when they went to
America." He ceased and sat down.

There was something divine in his indignation. Its
spirit moved in the dark places of their souls. They were
roused to anger, but it was no longer directed against the
truth-teller. The silence in which they sat was growing
restless. He himself was constrained to ease the tension
while the heroic fermentation was at work. Turning to the
father of the little guide at whose house he was to stay the
night, he could be heard asking in a conversational voice,
"Are you sure that I will not be giving too much trouble
to your wife and yourself this night?"

His host who had been resolving to beard Prendergast, the gombeen man, in the morning answered abstractedly. He assured him that a hundred thousand welcomes awaited him. Was not his wife putting on the griddle bread when he left the place over an hour ago? And did that not assure a welcome?

But the truth of his remarks was tearing at other breasts. Some of these were ignoble enough to bear resentment still for the discontent they aroused, a discontent which, instead of being divine, was contemptible, a discontent that sought to objectify its own shortcomings in a rival's faults. Who was the Organizer, anyway, to butt into farming? Loath they were to acknowledge to themselves that it was not farming he was butting into but ignorance and suspicion that lend themselves to oppression.

There was no one to tell them of the sacrifices he had made to combat these evils that lay at his very door— some were turning against him now—and to champion the downtrodden. There was no one to tell them what a fine spirit was dwelling among them. They could feel, but they could not measure the magnanimity of the man. How were they to recognize, when it dwelt amongst them, the Hero in man? How were they to know that this figure in his thin and sodden raincoat was the only man in Ireland who had the courage and the competence to stand up to the most popular writer in England when that writer, relying on his international success as an unchallenged bully, had calumniated weak and unpopular Ireland, never dreaming that there was spirit enough left in it to confront him and to answer him back? They had not read his *Open Letter*, so loved by lovers of freedom and so little ventilated by the press. This is what the man among them wrote to the great Jingo:

"If there was a high court of poetry, and those in power jealous of the noble name of poet, and that none of them should use it save those who were truly Knights of the Holy Ghost, they would hack the golden spurs from your heels and turn you out of the court. You had the ear of the world and you poisoned it with your prejudice. You had the power of song and you have always used it on behalf of the strong against the weak. You have smitten with all your might at creatures who are frail on earth but mighty in the heavens, at generosity, at truth, at justice. Heaven has withheld vision and power and beauty from you, for this your verse is but a shallow newspaper article made to rhyme. Truly ought the golden spurs be hacked from your heels and you be thrust out of the court."

Not only did he give him the lie, but he scoffed at him because his noblest sentiments were strictly on a cash basis.

When he arrived at the cottage, the children were in bed, so he had to content himself with gazing into cradle and cot.

"Only for that little man I might be floundering in a bog hole," he said as he smiled down at the eldest lad who had fallen suddenly asleep.

The farmer laughed drily. "God knows, sir, we are all floundering in a bog hole and we don't know how to get out."

He looked steadily at him over his glasses. "Why don't you all coöperate?"

"I think meself that they distrist Denroche who wants to be secretary and bookkeeper."

"But you can appoint your own secretary and book-keeper. He or she will be paid by the Central Council. If you cannot trust a local bookkeeper, the Council will appoint one and pay for the upkeep of a committee room until your society is self-supporting."

A voice from the kitchen called: "Musha, leave the gentleman alone until he has had a bite and sup. The table is laid."

Mrs. Fahy was unconsciously interrupting a talk that was about to bear fruit. Not noticing the plate full of eggs and bacon with soda bread and yellow butter beside it, the Organizer continued to help his host. "Why don't you yourself join the society in the next county if you and your neighbor will not form a society here?"

"There is Prendergast, the gombeen man. He would break me if I stirred."

"For how much are you on his books?"

Looking about him furtively, Fahy whispered a sum less than $120.

"Heavens, man, the Society will only be too glad to pay off that for you." Fahy hesitated. Seeing what was in his mind, the Organizer said. "No. They will not demand a mortgage on your house. They will charge no interest. You can take two or five years to pay it off out of profits. And, if it is a help to you, I will be your guarantor."

Mrs. Fahy emerged indignant. "Hadn't ye long enough in the Town Hall?" (You might have detected a sarcastic emphasis on the two words.) "Weren't yez there long enough to settle the country's problems without starving the poor man ye brought into the house?"

With that courtesy innate in Irish country folk, the neighbors waited until supper should be over. Now they began to appear in the doorway. They stood until the woman of the house should invite them. She opened the half door with, "Come in and sit down. But not a word out of ye until that poor man gets something to eat."

But the "poor man" was not thinking of food. He was telling them of their country's story that had been all but obliterated by a dead and colorless school system, by schools called ironically, "National Schools."

"Only the old men can tell you what I am telling you. When the old men are gone, the great glory of Ireland's past will have perished from the earth. The trader and the gombeen man will rule where once the Red Branch Knights won fame before Rome went down. Ireland, that stands yet for a country where things of the spirit are valued beyond material things, will come to be represented by the small trader; the wretched, timid, and downtrodden farmer; and the little rats that add halfpennys to pence and get a rake-off from every mouthful you eat and stitch you wear.

"But I will tell you of days before there were gombeen men to hold you down body and soul. Yes, I said soul, for you have not spirit enough left to call your souls your own. All your souls are worth is what you owe to Prendergast. Two thousand years ago there were men who ranged these hills with their mighty wolfhounds, hounds so big that they were bought to fight in amphitheatres of Roman

Gaul. Their names are not lost. Alone in Europe this country has preserved the names of the heroes who lie under their gigantic stones. The memory of the men who exulted in great feats and noble actions jealously guarded the champions of Ireland's heroic age. In England, Stonehenge stands, but no one who built it; in Brittany the dolmens are but nameless rocks. But here, in the deep earth of this country, lie men whose names are fresh in memory, the names of those they fought, the women they loved, and the names of their charioteers. Maeve, the great Queen of Connaught, sleeps in the county next to this under her grassy hill. The great green rath's sacred tomb lies heavy on the urns of the heroic men of old.

"Cuchulain is buried in Louth which he defended so well—and with it Ulster—when he held the ford against Maeve as she marched with the hosts of Connaught to take the Brown Bull. Let me tell you that story. War arose between the men of Ulster and the armies of Maeve in the west. The men of Ulster were put under a Druid spell, and only Cuchulain could defend their territory. He was called Cuchulain, who had been Setanta, because he had slain the fierce wolfhound that was the only guardian the smith of Ulla had. Smiths in those days were honored for their skill in subduing gold and bronze and making weapons and shields covered with golden bronze. At the banquets they sat at the high tables not far from the kings. So the Hound of the Smith, as he was called, stood alone against the hosts of Maeve. He stood in a shallow ford and not a champion that Maeve sent against him could pass. Maeve had promised her daughter to a great prince, the last great warrior of an old and almost ended race that was in Ireland long before the golden-haired and blue-eyed men came into it from over the seas. This Ferdia was Cuchulain's friend, for they had been taught the art of battle by famous warrior women who lived by the banks of the river on which Liverpool stands. They were companions in arms and unequalled in fight by any man save perhaps Fergus, the son of Roy.

"It went hard with Ferdia to face his friend and harder still with Cuchulain to oppose him, for he knew that he would be his death. Long they dashed together and fought till the water foamed about their knees. And the water was reddening now, for Ferdia was wounded sore. After a pause, and before renewing the struggle which each knew would be soon over for evermore, they kissed in the mid-battle. After that embrace Ferdia went down overwhelmed by the battle fury of the Hound. Remember 'hound' was an honorable title in those days.

"These were men who fought without rancor. They were warriors, and their delight was in battle. And these men were your forebears. They would not have been afraid of a gombeen man.

"Will I tell you of the warrior Finn, the son of Cool, and of his son, Ossian, who was the great epic poet of Ireland whose name still sounds in his son? His mother was Granu. Let me quote to you a poem that gives it all:

"Finn once o'ertook Granu, the golden haired,
     The fleet, the young,
 From her the lovely and from him the feared
     The primal poet sprung.

"Ossian! Two thousand years of mist and change
  Surround thy name;
Thy Fenian heroes now no longer range
  The hills of fame;
The very names of Gael and Gall seem strange;
  But thine the same
By miscalled moat and desecrated grange
  Remains, and shall remain.

You know 'Gall' means 'stranger.' It may have meant the
people who lived in the lands we now call France.

"Ossian loved Niav, the queen of fairyland. He rode
with her on her enchanted steed over the western sea.
Three hundred years passed and he hardly felt the time
go by. One day on the sea shore he saw an old spear shaft,
darkened with stains, washed up by the tide, and the old
longing for battle and hunting with his companions and
his father Finn came upon him. Telling of those hunts a
living poet sings:

"Kwelte, and Conan and Finn were there
  As we chased a deer with our baying hounds,
With Bran, Seogolan and Lomair,
  And passing the Druids' burial mounds,
Came to the cairn-heaped grassy hill
  Where passionate Maeve lies stony still.

Niav warned him that if he as much as touched earthly
ground even as lightly as a field mouse touches it, he
would never return.

"He rode off and at length came back to the scenes of
his youthful exploits. But all was changed. Finn and
Oscar and Dermot all were gone, and the land was filled

by singing monks. Some of these he saw trying to drag a
sack of sand to build a chapel. To help them, he leaned
from his horse and gave the sack a fling of yards in the
required direction. But the girthings broke. He touched
earth. His three hundred years fell upon him. In a second
the horse had disappeared. Old poets say that St. Patrick
found him and found it hard to make him repent and keep
his mind off his son Oscar and his father Finn McCool.

"I could tell you how Dermot eloped with Grainne and
of the song the King of the Fairies sang over their bed in
a cave of Ben Edair, a hill outside Dublin which is called
Howth now, a name given to it by the Danes who founded
the town one thousand years after Dermot and Grainne
slept in Ben Edair's cave."

He grew into himself and, with eyes entranced, hummed
as the fairy king might have intoned it, a snatch of fairy
song:

> "We who are old and gay,
>   O so old,
>   Thousands of years, thousands of years,
>   If all were told,

> "Give to these children new to the world
>   Peace far from men,
>   Is anything better, anything better?
>   Tell us it then."

His golden voice had as much magic in it as the song
itself. The blue eyes opened and smiled, gladdened by the
effect produced by poetry. Gloom lifted from the dark
men. They moved and uttered words of approval. One of

them declared himself reminded of something. Sternly
Mrs. Fahy pointed to the untouched plate. Out of the adjoining room a rapt voice came.

"Oh, sir, go on!"

"Whist in there, will ye?" said Mrs. Fahy.

After supper, over which his hostess stood guard, he lit
his pipe which had coltsfoot mixed with the tobacco to
make it burn slowly. It was through this slow-burning
tobacco that the disease was brought on which cost him
his life. But that is another story.

"You are always talking of your being Irishmen, but if
you were asked the history of your country, is there
among you one who knows it? Your forefathers did not sit
down paralyzed by grievances one hundred years old.
They were up and busy providing grievances for their
enemies. If you are determined 'to go on in the old way,' "
he smiled, "be sure that you make that way old enough."

But for Mrs. Fahy, he would have gone on talking into
the late hours of the morning as he had once done at
Yale when he was a guest of William Lyon Phelps, for he
was indefatigable.

It was some days after he had been driven by his host
to catch the early morning train that a body of men
dressed in their Sunday clothes—white shirts with the
collar buttons showing instead of a tie, and somber under
their dark hats—could be seen leaving the same station.
They were bound for the adjoining county, silent, like
men resolved. Maybe it was their resolution that made
them speak little to each other as if each were shy to have
his neighbor think that he could be moved by sentiment.

The object of their journey could be deduced from a re-mark of Fahy: "There's one thing certain: Prendergast can do damn all to us if we stick together."

The Hero in man had not altogether gone in that earlier morning train.

Dublin Revisited i: The Town

Most PEOPLE MUST HAVE EX-
perienced the anticipation and the excitement that comes
from the lifting of the window blind of a strange bedroom
of a morning. These were my experiences as I raised the
blind of Room 37 in the Shelbourne Hotel. I did not know
on which side of the house I was, for I had arrived late in
the night; but I knew that, no matter which side it was, I
would look out upon a familiar scene.

Late at night I heard solitary footsteps moving along
what I guessed must be Kildare Street, that flanks the
Shelbourne on the west. I lay, and gave thanks for the
silence that made such sound audible, and for the roomi-
ness of the town. Into my head came the lines of my pecul-
iar friend, Alabaster. I repeated them and slept.

> " 'Tis sweet to hear the p'liceman's heavy feet
>   Beat thick-soled comfort to our cozy homes;
>   'Tis sweet to see his lanthorn in the street
>   Grow broader and look brighter as he comes."

What I heard must have been the thick-soled comfort
of the guardian of the citizens' repose.

Yes, it was Kildare Street. I was on a level with the

roofs of three or four houses: valleys and gables with their little slates not bigger than playing cards and, most charming of all, the stout chimney stacks with their dozen or half-dozen chimney pots, one or two with the morning smoke rising: breakfast was cooking. The drowsy citizens were turning in their beds. Those chimney pots, built deliberately for utility, how they have come, like so many things after two hundred years, to have a beauty all their own!

Sideways, to the left, I could see the lake in Stephen's Green, not called after James Stephens as it should have been—had Dublin not been notorious in disregarding its great men. Then, beyond, the faint curves of the Dublin Mountains that wall Wicklow—"The Garden of Ireland."

Back to my unfriendly, friendly, bitter Ithaca after six years! There will be plenty to discover and changes to observe.

The bathroom was large, large as a bedroom. It had in all likelihood been a bedroom before it was converted into a luxurious bathroom—every tap, bolt and bit of brasswork polished, and thick rugs on the floor—truly a well-cherished hotel. What a relief from the dirty, slipshod room I had left in war-worn London. The soft Vartry water comes steaming from the faucet without delay. It was seven-thirty and I wanted to fill the tub so I could float in peace.

"Welcome back!" a voice exclaimed.

I heard the genial and ingratiating voice with a laugh in it which discounted the geniality a little, inasmuch as it suggested that my return to Dublin was a part of a great farce or joke, part of the great joke that the owner of the voice considered life to be. And, to give him his due, he did not except his own.

"Run to earth," I said to myself. "And I not back ten hours!" "Run to water," would have been more fitting, seeing that I was half-submerged in my bath.

"Is that you, Pope?" I shouted through the closed door.

Now "The Pope" was one of a family of brothers, for the like of which you would have to go to the pages of Turgenev. Gallus boys all! He was christened "The Pope" by his brother, "The Bird," in derision for his addiction to devotion when he was a boy. He had outsoared and bidden *Good-bye to All That*. Gallus boys of a great family, the Sire of which lived to a hundred years and died a respected citizen. So much so, that all license was allowed to the boys and expected. They fell not short of expectations. And that is saying a great deal when you come to think of Dublin.

"I knew it was you," I added.

"Who the devil else did you think it was? Let me in."

"You can't come in; the place is full of steam."

"It wouldn't be the first Turkish bath I was in."

It was true. Many were the dawns that had found him sleeping in the Hammam in the good old days; as most days become, provided they are a long time past. So what could I do but open the door?

In he came and took a look at me from side to side much as a boxing promoter might eye a white hope.

"Not too bad," he exclaimed. And the mirth bubbled out of him, notwithstanding the fact that it was before eight in the morning, and that was early as things go in the old town.

"I saw you got back," he said.

So that was it! I was in the papers. Not for nothing had an editor sent his men to intercept me at the airport and the pier. Because of that I had gone to bed feeling proud and important. I began to lose that feeling now. Soon I would be neither proud nor important when the greatest story-distorter in Dublin had done with me. He was putting me to the question now.

"How did you like the States?"

This is where I have to be careful, I reminded myself, for in the States a joke is liable to be misconstrued, especially when it has to travel three thousand miles.

"Right well," I said, "or I would not have spent six years there. They have everything. Their mode of living is profusion and they want you to share it with them."

Then a great idea struck me. If I am to be misquoted, let me be quoted for something harmless and inoffensive, something that he will go around saying; and let those who can, see the joke.

I could see that he was disconcerted. So I gave him something to twist:

"It was the potato famine drove me out."

"Potato famine? Have they no potatoes?"

"Lashings," I said, "but they don't know how, or they won't cook them as they should be cooked. You never see a potato bursting floury from its jacket in the States. The potato famine in Ireland drove hundreds of thousands to America. But the same famine there drove me back."

I caught his bird's eye on my pajamas. I threw a towel over them. Too late! I could hear his mind chalking them up. He will report me now as a sissy or a millionaire.

"How did you get back?"

"On the *Queen Mary:* four days."

"Four days?"

"Yes; but speed was nullified by our having to wait two days at anchor in the Firth of Clyde. We arrived in Scotland on a Sunday. We had to wait for a tender but there was no service, barring religious service which doesn't serve to set us on an earthly shore."

"They were all soused."

"They were all Sabbatharians," I differentiated. "We got to London by a night train and arrived at Euston where even the cloak rooms were crowded out—women porters trundling barrows—congestion and overcrowding everywhere. Many of the restaurants have become semi-automats where you wait in a queue with your tray. In some you can get only one cup of tea, for they are short of milk. Hotels are worn out. The town is full of shell holes showing cellars and subterranean passages overgrown with dandelions and loosestrife. You can see St. Paul's from the most unexpected places. There is hardly a pane of glass in the shops. In Fetter Lane the face is blown out of Mooney's clock. Even the houses that look all right are condemned for cracked walls or broken sewerage. There are American and Canadian troops everywhere, the most patient and disciplined and best behaved men I ever saw. The citizens are exhausted and show it. A dirty and shoddy town."

But he was not interested. He wanted to get to the scandals:

"The Spanish Grandee is dead. The Major still keeps coming into the tavern by a different door every time. The Colonel is under restraint and the Marquis died on his honeymoon."

"Listen," I said, as I got back into the hot water, "that's nothing. We had a senator in the States who collapsed in the train on his honeymoon. You cannot beat the States, when it comes to sudden death."

He thought so hard that the tip of his nose twitched. I knew what was on his mind; he did not like the idea of sudden death. To cheer him I said, "You are the last one to worry, you with that magnificent longevity in your family, you with a father that lived to a hundred."

He was not comforted, at least not suddenly. He cogitated a little more and then said, as if to discount my consolation, "He died at ninety-six."

"Ninety-six, nonsense! You must have seen him with his back to the light. He made the century and you'll do likewise unless you take to politics or patriotism."

So far the interview was unsatisfactory. He had nothing on me yet. But give him time. Meanwhile, if I listen and evince interest, I'll hear everything that has happened during my absence.

He brightened and exclaimed, "Aw! Here's a good one: did you hear about Dev?"

Now one reason I left Dublin was that I could no longer sustain the load of loathing for humbug, which I have detested all my life. And to bring up this impersonation of casuistry, hypocrisy and humbug on the very moment of my return was, to say the least, disheartening.

"No," I said firmly, "and I don't want to hear of him. He looks too much like a laugh in mourning to interest me."

"But it will interest you to hear that he has become a sugar daddy." He smiled and took a seat on my pajamas. Now when it comes to impugning a man's private life (even unjustly), that is quite another thing. I'll stand up any day for the sanctity of the home.

"I don't believe a word of it," I said. "If he is good for anything, he is a good husband."

Slowly he smiled in a superior and condescending way. "I thought that would get you. You got me wrong. Dev has become the sugar daddy of Europe. He is handing out our sugar to the Continent and leaving us short at home."

"Oh, so that is what you mean by a sugar daddy," I replied. "I suppose he will say that he has got a mandate from the Tourist Development Association to leave the country short of sugar while handing out the makings of diabetes to the Continent. Let us keep away from *Weltpolitik* and tell me what has become of Fergus who started a selective hotel in the West?"

He pushed his bowler hat on to the back of his head. "Now that you mention him. He was missing for a time, but he must be in the pink. Look at this. Can you beat it? I might go there myself. This can only have come from him."

He looked into his pocketbook and selected the following advertisement which he wanted me to look at; but I called to him to read it aloud. I couldn't handle it in my bath. With a laugh at every stop he read:—

"Young (18-30) lady companion-housekeeper, some knowledge and taste for cooking, preferably capable drive car, fond of country life, wanted; comfortable, modern, country house hotel, remote West Eire; work not hard; must have pleasant looks, lively, cheerful personality; willingness to try hand at anything; interest, pictures, music, Irish national culture—dancing, language; also bathing, games, etc., an advantage; preferably no nail pigment, lipstick, ultra-modern, stupid fashion audacities; personality, character. Good looks more important than certificates, diplomas.—B.C. 1009, Box 60."

Fergus to the life, I thought. Good looks are more than all the rest. He puts them in the place where emphasis falls, at the end. Where is this Thélème that he has built in the West?

Dancing, language, lively; would he have them wince and wriggle more? I asked myself. Why, if a girl had half these accomplishments, I mused, there would be no need of further "character." Any more would be superfluous. In America she would be on the Olympic team for half a dozen events.

"Go down and order breakfast," I finally said. "I will join you in ten minutes."

As I left the hotel, I took a turn to the left along Merrion Row. "The One-Eyed Man" had changed hands—most taverns do. It is Durkin's now; now it is Sweeney's. What is it that the old gloss written by a monk on the

edge of his parchment said about a field? It had many
landlords. "But the kings lie under the sod." The field
kept on. So it is with the Dublin pubs, but the change is
quicker.

When I came to the end of the block, I turned again to
the left. I should have been in Merrion Street with the
government buildings on the left and opposite them the
house that held the infant Duke of Wellington but now
houses the Land Commission that dominates more "fields"
than ever the Iron Duke did. Yes, I was in Merrion
Street; but I was also in the eighteenth century. The air
was crystal clear, even the thin blue plumes of turf smoke
could not stain the sky as the soft coal had done before
the town had won back to its own. I could see the wide
greens of Leinster Lawn and Merrion Square. In front of
me was Number One where the forceful and brisk father
of Oscar Wilde practiced and won an international
reputation as an oculist and aurist. Here his wife, Spe-
ranza, held her exotic salons. How spacious and clean the
town is. Let me never hear that facile bit of misleading
alliteration, "dirty Dublin," again. It is the cleanest town
I have been in for years and I have seen seventy or more.
What room there is—forty yards between the groups of
people! And no one is in a hurry. No dogs to be seen.
After all, the Irish are a race of sportsmen and they do
not tie dogs up in towns to make the ways filthy and the
food unclean from the dessicated dung. Their setters, ter-
riers and running dogs are where all dogs should be—in
the country.

Sixty yards away I spotted Charlie Boyce coming

along with his friend, Drury. Not a day older, either of them. No credit to me to recognize Boyce. Many's the time I saw his skilful hands steering the latest thing in automobiles along the streets. Had he cared to use those beautiful hands of his, he could have been a better oculist or surgeon than ever Sir William Wilde was. But no; he preferred to give anesthetics.

And they recognized me!

"What's come over us?" I asked. "You two are not a day older and I have been away for six years."

They had not realized that time had forgotten them and me. And to think of Drury asking me if I remembered him. Well, well. We had not exchanged many sentences when the interview began to grow a little awkward. Were they in a hurry? That could hardly be. I never saw anyone in Dublin who was in a hurry except Nolan Whelan, and that was to change the venue. More likely they were beginning to be bored with me. And who was I to blame them? I have so often been bored by myself. Rather fatuously I said, "Ha! Ha! You are on your way to the club where there are gold stars in a deep-blue ceiling and a bee's wing in every bottle of port? They serve it slanting."

They did not answer, perhaps because it was a little early; but reticence does not obscure the fact that it is the most respectable club in town—"The Friendly Brothers." What a perfect name for a club! But this one is a little bit too exclusive for my choice. For instance, it excludes me. It would exclude me more, if I were proposed for membership, for "I dig," as the saying is, when I dig at all—I am *pareus et infrequens* as a digger—with the other foot. Nevertheless, it must be delightful to belong to a religion wherein a club takes the part of a church. It takes a reverent care of its members too; and its members guard its reputation in return.

I was just passing the office of the attorneys who paid James Stephens a minimum wage to do their scrivening. It was next door to my old friend, Sir Lambert Ormsby, who used to serve sloke with the mutton; and as he used to say, "All I want is a little respect." Yes; that's what we all will want when we grow old: "Honor, love, obedience; troops of friends," friendly brothers!

Suddenly the awful thought struck me. Why had I not had my wits about me when I made that foolish remark beginning with "Ha! Ha!" Why the "Ha! Ha!"? I should have known that they were on their way to some sort of service or other. It was early and it was Sunday, wasn't it? Oh, my God! That is why they were taking their anticipated pleasure seriously. They probably thought that I knew it, and they must have all the more resented my admonishing "Ha! Ha!"

On either side, a greensward spread in our most spacious town, a town that could boast spacious days of its own not a hundred years ago. Merrion Square and Leinster Lawn still kept their railings. London had given up the metal work of her public and private enclosures to the war.

I went by Lincoln Place. It is easy to pass it now. "Indignation House" has changed hands as "The One-Eyed Man" has. And Fannin is in retirement somewhere in

Sandymount where he probably reserves his contempt for the ex-police sergeants who wade on the Strand to cure their corns.

If you enter Trinity College by the back gate, you have the pathology school to your left and, behind it, Finn's Hotel whence James Joyce eloped with Nora Barnacle forty years ago. And the school of chemistry is on your right. It was here that Professor Emerson Reynolds taught chemistry with such wholehearted enthusiasm that he invaded with it even the theological school. Forty years ago! And now chemistry and every other kind of science is taking over from the theologians. Science has sterilized our day.

The beautiful sward of the park spreads out level before the eye: many's the time I circled its athletic field—four laps to the mile, and the finish over there along by the trees under which sat the town's elite with their trailing skirts and their gaily colored parasols. Ah, me!

On the left the electric trams run along the raised street behind the trees and they make no sound.

In silence I walked upon the grass. What an oasis the park makes in the center of the city! And the silence! To its cleanliness you may well add its civilization when you are clearing the fair name of Dublin of all the calumnies of the past. "Dirty Dublin" indeed! I had to travel over more than half the world to realize how clean and beautiful Dublin is. It is not yet completely cursed by the stucco palaces of modern vulgarity. Ruskin's influence built that dark-gray pile over there with windows arched and embellished in lighter stone, the engineering school

that takes up one side of the New Square in which haw-
thorns and holm oaks spread. Three sides of gray stone,
and on the fourth, the gabled houses of Queen Anne, cased
in red brick, before you pass the great library to which
every book published in Great Britain goes by law.

In the second house from the corner dwelt my beloved
mentor, Henry Stuart McCran, Hegelian and Humanist.
He would quote: "While I am, Death is not. When Death
is, I am not."

"So you see, my dear fellow," he would say, "the two
never meet." Thus he showed how Epicurus tried to rid
the mind of thanatophobia, the fear of death. In that
subtlety of the Greek there was little consolation, for it's
the dying that hurts. Ah, there's the rub. The chief consolation, if any, and a comfort in our doom, is that death
is universal.

"Death cannot be an evil, because it is universal," said
Goethe in one of his lighter moments. But so is disease;
and it manages to be an evil in spite of its universality.
The best we can say for ourselves is that, for better or for
worse, we are all in the same boat. And, seeing that this
is so, there is a lot to be said for the philosophy of "The
Friendly Brothers," who remain friendly in the boat during its passage, even if they limit and select the passengers.

On the left of the graceful campanile stands, newly
built, a temple of Nike to those alumni of Dublin University who fell in the last war. There is also a statue to
Lecky. But where are the others? *Cetera desunt.* Burke
and Goldsmith stand in bronze without the walls in the
narrow arc of grass that is all that is left of College Green.

Where are Swift, Hamilton, Molyneux and Moore?
Moore is round the corner. And the others are in the great
library, stuccoed between the books.

In the front courtyard two branches of the old oaks
have fallen, one from each; and my two old friends are
gone. The second, the sweetest cynic of all time, Robert
Yelverton Tyrrell who, with the great Mahaffy, represented the whole College to Oscar Wilde before Mahaffy
expelled that young man to Oxford.

The noon sun is pouring down peacefully in the closes.
Where are the Fellows, the Dons, the Scholars of the
House, and the Provost? I look toward the back door of
the Provost's House. Through that little, dark and forbidding postern in the years gone by I went once or twice
in trepidation, when summoned to appear for a reprimand
in the Provost's House.There is no one about now at high
noon. The cobblestones of the front square that sounded
to so many famous feet are silent. There is not a sound to
be heard from the town outside. What can have happened
to the greatest educators in Europe? I have it! It is high
noon; they are communing with the Muses. They are all
nympholept. And so am I.

Dublin Revisited ii: The Country

$\mathcal{I}\!s$ THERE ANYTHING MORE annoying or calculated to fill you with resentment and impatience than the fatuous question, "Do you believe in fairies?"—a question usually accompanied by a somewhat sneering superiority and patronage? I, for one, resent it just as I would resent the question of a know-it-all who inquired, "Do you believe in ideas?" It is the same sort of vexation that is caused by a waiter who familiarly declares what you like before you are given a chance to order it, and it arises from an attempt on the part of a person to include your power of percipience in his own. What makes such a question obnoxious is the logic of the questioner and the imputation in the word "belief" with all its undistributed meanings. Added to this, there is the deep conviction within you that all such matter-of-fact people are utterly incapable of understanding what instinct is, or the gift whereby the diviner is empowered to find water, or the unsophisticated poet to reach the heart, or the man or woman who is fey to see fairies. This conviction makes you resent such fact-frozen souls; you feel resistance and you sense a lack of sympathy. You know that they would scoff at and destroy, if they could, the procreant omnipotence of the unconscious mind.

Such inquisitorial persons are frequently found. They have only a limited time to put their question, and neither time nor attention to hear you out. Their minds are self-contained and already made up. My way of dealing with such quidnuncs is to retort with another question. When they repeat, "Do you believe in fairies?" I ask, "What, here?" I will admit that this is almost too disconcerting to be polite; but then who can imagine a translunary visitor in Times Square?

From this it will be obvious that time and place are everything. The first step to take, then, is to get out of the eighteenth century. And in getting away from it, to look back upon it from a standpoint of sanitation and commiseration. Far from the fetid stews and the lazar houses of this age of reason are the gay, mischievous, and appeasable fairy denizens of rath and hill.

Though they partake not of human food, they suffered from the potato famine when millions of those who had eyes to see or spells whereby to placate them, closed their eyes forever or turned them away from the mystic circles around the twisted thorn. Mass schooling and regimented education blinded many, and shut many a mind to their immemorial lore.

"Troth, Sir," said Darby Doolin to Sir William Wilde, "what betune them national boords and Godless Colleges, and other sorts of larnin', and the loss of the 'pratey, and the sickness, and all the people that's goin' to America, and the craturs that's forced to go into the workhouse, or is dyin' off in the ditches, and the clargy settin' their faces agin them, and telling the people not to *give in* to them, sarra wan of the Gintry (cross about us!) will be found in the country, nor a word about them or their doin's in no time."

Thus in beautiful musical speech was announced the defection of the fairies almost one hundred years ago. But the fairies are immortal; they may withdraw, but they cannot be destroyed. They avoided commissioners, inspectors, school boards, and examinations; survived their plague- or famine-stricken cultivators, and withdrew into the Many-Colored Land amid the purple mountains and the long, dark, green, reedy valleys of the West. Sir William Wilde, who knew their language, bears witness to this fact in the following words:

"The fairies—the whole pantheon of Irish demigods—are retiring one by one from the habitations of man to the distant islands where the wild waves of the Atlantic raise their foaming crests; or they have fled into the mountain passes and have taken up their abodes in those wild, romantic glens—lurking in the gorgeous yellow furze and purple heath, amidst the savage, disrupted rocks, or creeping beneath the warrior's grave."

Well do I know where they are! I have lived longer in Iol Daitthé, the Many-Colored Connemara, than Sir William Wilde. The best thing I can do is to follow them up. One thing is certain: they will not visit the East of Ireland in my time. Therefore my immediate problem is how to go after them with transportation all muddled as it is now. And I knew that first I would find many of my acquaintances.

I am very careful to refrain from saying that Ireland's a strange country, just as I deny myself comment on the faces I see in a restaurant, because I am always mindful that I myself am a part of the show. This is what George Bernard Shaw forgot when, after reading Joyce, he exclaimed, "If such characters really exist in Dublin, there should be a Commission to enquire, 'Why?'" He should have known: he was born in Dublin. But he left it as soon as possible, you will object. That matters not. Dean Swift was only born in Dublin. That was enough!

As I say, I am never unmindful that I am part of the *mise en scène*. Suppose, conversely, that my friends are but a part of myself. Well? I am not ashamed of them. There is not one of them whom you could call regulated, stereotyped, standardized, pedestrian or ordinary. Not one! Now before me stood Dulcey! Her eyes were of that strange blue that is not light blue nor violet, and yet, not a deep one-colored blue, but of a blue that overcame the gray around the large pupils that were level with my own. The light was sharp. Those eyes would be deep violet in a room.

She stood in front of me and said not a word, but smiled slowly. She watched my eyes, waiting for recognition to dawn. I waited for it too, as I looked at her neck with its smooth Irish skin. Up came the memory of Robin. I remembered, "It's more matey." That was his explanation for sleeping in so narrow a bed. How sweet was her smile, the smile of a goodhearted, companionable woman. Before she could say, "You don't know me," I said, "But it's you that are looking well."

"You have been a long time away."

"Six years. And I can say that you have not altered. What are you doing? Where are you living now?"

She told me that she was married and the mother of three. She made a joke, smiling, and I caught a glimpse of her even teeth.

"And have you forgotten Robin?"

"Could I ever forget him? Those were the days!"

She smiled regretfully, the mother of three, for the days when there was nothing bounded by a golden ring. I marveled at the power Robin had over women. And he was "rantin' rovin'" if a lad ever was. Bald and by no means good-looking, yet he had a way with women. Maybe his deep voice and his dark eyes mesmerized them, and the way he had of taking everything for granted. How Dulcey regretted him.

"With that fine figure and your regular features and your silken skin, I hope you married well. Though, as a rule, the lovelier the woman the more undeserving the man —in this country, anyway," I said.

"I live in the country. In Robin's Wicklow," she replied. "And though it brings back many memories, I can't complain."

"Will you ever forget the trailer?" I asked.

She forgot to look embarrassed, but laughed gaily.

"You are asking *me*," she answered and pointed to herself.

I went on—" 'Will none of you blighters never laugh?'

he used to say when he would come into a pub to meet his friends. He never gave himself a chance."

On this we agreed, nodding knowingly.

She shook hands and went away, leaving me with mingled memories and thoughts that were sad and glad. Sad, because Robin was gone, though it was just in time before old age caught up with him; and glad that Dulcey, for all her badinage, had got what she so well deserved, a happy fireside clime.

What I am going to say now can be, or used to be, said only of the saints. Dulcey has not yet been classified in that category, and I hope that her days on her farm will be long; but she has one characteristic of the saints, that is, of a few of them: she has fragrance. Now I hate perfumes, as Horace did; but Dulcey had no need to use them. She had a fragrance all her own. I recalled what the poets said about a fragrant breath without believing it; I took it for something super-physiological until I met Dulcey: breath or body, there it was, fragrance; Dulcey diffused it. She was the only one I ever met who could.

They tell me that Ida of Louvain, St. Colette and St. Humiliana were as fragrant as sweet flowers. St. Herman Joseph could be traced through the corridors by the rare perfumes he scattered. St. Thomas Aquinas smelled of male frankincense; and I myself knew a lay brother who smelled of snuff. None of these explain Dulcey, who before her marriage was not noticeably a saint.

Even Robin's crazy caravan would be welcome now! There are no automobiles, for there is no fuel. And as for the trains—you have to be at the station two hours before the train is scheduled to depart, and then there's no guarantee of a seat. Spending hours in a queue—that's what I cannot do. And it is just as well. I heard lately of a man who stood in a queue at a station for an hour and a half to buy a ticket. He could tolerate it no longer, so he tried to take his seat in the train.

"Where's your ticket?" the stationmaster asked.

"The office was not open, though I waited for over an hour in the queue. When is the office opened?" the man said.

"God only knows!" the stationmaster said, and moaned despairingly. "It may never be open, but you should have got your ticket just the same."

With a difficulty like that before me, the Many-Colored Land seems far away. "It is better to be born lucky than rich," I mused. I was not born rich, though my parents were well to do. So I may say—and it is borne out by experience—I was born lucky. Emphatically so. For immediately I met Harrington. His Chrysler was fitted in front of the hood with a contraption that looked at first sight like a cauldron for boiling tar.

"Carbon gas," said he. Then he added, when he heard of my longing to go West, "I will drive you there."

We started out right after lunch and threaded daintily through the streets.

Soon an impressive column came in sight, the obelisk that Connolly, the Great Commoner in the days of Grattan's parliament, built to end a vista through the woods of Castletown. "Connolly's Folly" they call it who are ignorant both of history and the way the great men lived.

But my friend was not interested, and we rolled along merrily, considering ourselves, of course, as exceptions and superiors to the general life of the nation, as I am inclined to do when I imagine that I stand apart from all that goes to the making of the amalgam that is I. After all, what am I? I asked myself, but a composite creation of Mahaffy, Tyrrell, Macran, Bury (to go backwards), Seumas O'Sullivan, Boyce, Drury, Pope Flanagan, Bob Ussher, Harrington and Dulcey Fielding (for which I ought to be grateful, and I am), Keven Smith, Hugh Harpur, the Major (yes; I know I should be grateful) and the men behind them, George Bonass and Boyd-Barrett, who are gone. Maybe, for we must be just, it is not fair on them that they should be represented severally by me. But it should make them take thought (if they only knew it) and go easy and be lenient in their judgment, because when they are depreciating me, for all they know they may be disparaging themselves. Can you blame any Dubliner for being variegated and anent, that is, referable to all that has gone before?

Athlone is the center of Ireland and the very place to cable from if you want to cable from the heart of the island. Now that we are in Athlone, it will not be long until we enter Connaught where "The Others" still sojourn. "The Others" are "immortal, mild, proud shadows" and are visible only to enchanted eyes.

In a picture by Jack Yeats of a bowed countryman doubled with toil and hardship, leading a wretched donkey and cart along an exposed and endless road with only one windswept tree beside it, "The Others" may be seen, stately, clothed in dim gold, and majestic, a vision which is the dream of the man, his treasure and his strong sustenance—a splendor which is the very opposite to his lot. By the reedy pools, the twisted thorns and the windy bogs that here and there island a fair green knoll or give way to rock and golden whin, "The Others" have come to dwell. Their courts are richer than if they were held over the deep fields of Moate or Mullingar because in those prosperous pastures live no men with minds capable of a longing strong enough to bring "The Others" nigh to hand. Their thoughts or their feelings are not intense enough to endow hill, rath or glen with vision that may be reflected back, as by a mental radar, to the next recipient mind. This is what the mechanics of "seeing the fairies" may be reduced to: terms as simple as scientific terms. The day is not far off when such terms may be synonymous.

The mental image of the desirable is cast upon "airy mountain" or "rushy glen" and gathered again by those with eyes to see. But why reduce the immortals to human reason? Why use the debased coinage of pros and cons? Away with reason! I am not addressing hucksters. I am in the Land of Many Colors now. To my scientific transporter with the fuel gas I have bidden good-bye.

What territory could be more worthy of lordly vision than this land beyond the Shannon and the slowly winding Suck? Far away rise the tumbling mountains diamonded by a flash of sunlight or merging into majesty in purple and gold. Beyond them, the illimitable Atlantic with its spectral islands seen once in seven years. There floated the Isle of Inis Bofin, the Island of the White Cow, until it was accidentally disenchanted by some fishermen who touched it with fire. It could no longer float about, hidden in mist from mortal eyes, for fire with its power to disenchant fixed it forever on its base.

This is the way that came about. From Omey Island, which can be reached from the mainland at low tide, went a fisherman and his son with a seed of fire in turf laid on clay to broil their catch. They heard about them the song of birds and the sounds of sheep and lambs. They thought they had reached Hy Brasil and landed, bringing their fire with them. They beheld a "Lady full beautiful" driving a cow, no mere animal, to a lake. She touched the cow and it turned into stone. One of the men went to remonstrate with her when, instantly, she became a rock. But, before any disaster, the White Cow can be seen on the island, which is inhabited by mortals now. Though the Cow and its lovely herd are petrified, yet nothing has happened to the fairies who can be heard carousing on the hills. They tempt men to eat their fairy food by throwing down showers of fish. A man who was going by the rath side of a fort, was struck with an iris leaf by one of its inhabitants. He drew his black-hafted knife and stabbed the elf. Otway, who tells the tale, records how the fairy-killer, terrified by what he had done, ran for help, and, on returning with some men, found only a heap of slime "like what a dead frog turns into" on the spot. An Englishman who owned the island, and lived there until recently, was told that he was surrounded, one day when he went out shooting, by a troop of fairy girls dressed in brown.

Reluctant as I am to deal with facts, this may be a

good opportunity to solace and, for a while, silence them with scientifically ascertainable particulars: the mirage and the submergence of the coast. Off the shore where Letter Hill subsides toward the ocean, I have seen the remains of a pine forest with its stumps of trees about three feet high, protruding from the sea bed at low tide. It is hard by the "Cave of the Women" (a roofless gully now) where the naked bodies of two young women were found years ago while its roofs still held against the assaults of the breakers and it was still a cave. This is where the Merman appeared shortly after the last war. But I do not require mundane proof for immortal things. The late T. J. Westropp, a valued friend, told me of many happenings which he set down in print from old records. O Brazile, the Enchanted Island, was seen by multitudes off the Ulster coast in 1663. One Captain John Nesbitt settled in Killybegs and traded with France. On a voyage in March, 1675, he found himself in a dense fog off an unknown island in less than three fathoms. He and eight persons—three fully named—saw it. He and three officers landed and saw woods, cattle, horses, sheep and black rabbits. The travelers came to a castle, but no person answered them. They returned and lit a fire, for the evening was cold; but a hideous noise ensued, and they took the boat and fled to the ship. Next day they saw a gentleman and his servants on the shore and brought them off. He said that he had long been imprisoned in the castle by an enchanter, but the lighting of a fire by Christians had wrecked the main tower and broken the spell. Nesbitt brought them to Killybegs, where many, many believed their story on seeing their old coins and hearing their out-of-date language and ideas. So much for that; but as for out-of-date ideas, this country is full of them at the present time. No account of a visit to it could be complete without an example. Here is a quotation from the *Stars and Stripes*: "And certainly Dublin is the only capital where Franco is spoken of seriously as a defender of Christiandom, and regarded as a hopeful bulwark to a Communist Europe." And—another hallucination—"Meanwhile, Ireland's 60,000 regulars and two squadrons of training aircraft—which are mostly armed by the British—gathered around the northern border to repel more than a million American and British getting ready to march over from Ulster."

Without insisting on rationalization, it is possible that the gentleman and his servants rescued from the enchanter and his enchanted island may have been descendants of some survivors of the Spanish Armada wrecked upon the western shores. The Spanish strain in him would account for his out-of-date ideas and the Irish island for the enchantment of man and beast.

The Tuatha de Danaans hid in "floating islands, with a wind that evermore keeps them out of sight of shore." They had spells by which wind and mist were controlled. Sir Samuel Ferguson in his poem, which has for its subject Aideen's grave on the Hill of Howth, tells how that island was then protected:

> And when the fierce de Danaan ghosts
> At midnight from its peaks come down;
> And all around the enchanted coasts
> Despairing strangers drown.

It is strange that the leprechaun is not mentioned or feared on the islands off the western coast of Ireland. This would seem to buttress up a favorite theory of my own concerning the origin of the leprechaun, the fairy cobbler skilled in leather and dressed in leather gaily colored, "green jacket, red cap and white owl's feather": the mischievous and willful little man who had to be watched continually and who could steal away a human child or put a spell upon cattle. What else is he but the little Laplander who, coming out of the Arctic darkness, harassed the thorps of the Danes before those raiders settled in Ireland and brought with them their racial memory of the Lap-rechaun, brightly dressed even to the present time? And so strong was that memory that they may be seen now at propitious moments between the light and the dark. The absence of the leprechaun from the outermost islands on which the Danes never settled bears out my theory that he is a familiar only of the Danish "spheres of influence."

Writing of poetry, A. E. Housman asked, "How many have an organ by which to perceive it?" The answer was, very few. And it may well be asked what qualifications have I to discuss fairies; am I fey? Those hard-headed sons of light, the poets Edmund Spenser and W. B. Yeats, were able to put their minds out of clutch and align themselves closely with the Muses. Neither of them claims to have seen a ghost. I have seen a ghost, and so, in the nature of things, although not a dreamer, I have a sense of the haunts of the fairies and a love for the half-light on moor and hill.

I saw a ghost one day when driving in the Phoenix Park. I was slowing the car as it approached Castleknock Gate, and thinking of nothing, when on the grass margin on the right-hand side of the road, a horseman came along on a bay horse. He was dressed in a brown riding coat, a checkered waistcoat, and he wore a bowler hat. There was no mistaking his face with its nose bent sideways and its horsy look. As he passed, he raised his whip. I thought nothing of it. He was not a close acquaintance of mine. He did what a casual acquaintance would do, and I saluted him. There was no need to stop. As I was about to go through the gate, suddenly it came to me:—he was dead; dead this three months or more. I looked back at once. He had vanished. The meaninglessness of his appearing to me who hardly knew him, and my thinking no more of it than the inconsequent occurrences in a dream alone are enough to put him in the category of genuine apparitions. They appear for no reason on earth. Never will you see a leprechaun if you go to look for one deliberately.

"Those who hear fairy music are usually not educated enough to take it down. I wish I could hear it. I have tried time and again." This remark was made by the first person I meet in Iol Daitthé!

There is a young man here in the house where I am staying. He is writing an opera, for he is a well-known and skilled composer, a serious-minded student. And he is here with more than a belief in the fairies: he has a practical use for them. He is waiting to catch their enchanted airs.

"Do you know what happens to those who hear fairy music?" I asked.

"I don't care," he replied. "We have lost an awful amount of precious material. We must recover as much as we can."

I said no more but meditated on the strange fact that there was hardly any harmony before John Dunstable, an exponent of counterpoint, combined melodies in the fifteenth century. But the many-stringed harp was known in Ireland in the sixth century and we know there was choral singing. It is now the music of a lost kingdom. I hope that my accomplished composer will catch, when he is little thinking of it (there is no other way), that wild music as he walks among the windy hills. As a sop to the sceptical, I may add an assurance I had from Marconi: "Nothing that sounded once is lost."

Yes, it is true. And the force that makes men "give in" to the fairies is the force of the imagination without which a nation has nothing to contribute to mankind. In revisiting Ireland it was not to see Connolly's Folly, or to inquire how far the present Government is to blame for the inconsistencies and muddles of the present time, but to find if memories of the rosy dawn still colored the minds of men. There will be other tenants in the Fort of Rathangan; but nothing can bring back, if once they be lost, the "old beautiful mythologies wherein ancient man said symbolically all he knew about God and man's soul."

The Merriman

The CAR STOOD READY FOR A journey of about two hundred miles, for we were to spend Christmas in the West of Ireland. As I was about to take my seat, a triangular piece of newspaper caught my eye. It lay on the running board, plastered down by the rain, and its print was as dark as the rubber covering underneath. I was about to push it off with my shoe when I read:

STRANGE STORY BY FISHERMEN

MERMAN SEEN OFF THE CONNEMARA COAST

Yesterday two fishermen, John Heanue and Robert Wallace, on their way home after a day's fishing, stated that they saw a strange human-like creature standing waist high in eight feet of water in the Cave na Mblan west of Renvyle. As their boat approached, he . . ."

It broke off tantalizingly. But I saw the date, October 1. I could decipher no more. October: two months ago. West of Renvyle! I was just going there. What a coincidence! I could not explain what brought that torn notice to my attention or what stuck it to the running board. I have long ago given up trying to explain coincidences. I had never heard of a merman. Mermaids, yes; but this was new to me and off the very coast where I lived for parts of the year. Thank God for the Unknowable. I didn't care how the newspaper came to be where it was; all I cared for now was to interview those two fishermen. I was sure that I knew them, though I may not have known them by name. I hoped that they hadn't been made taciturn and suspicious by too many interviews, for that is the way country folk become if questioned about the supernatural by strangers. To those who dwell in the immemorial and haunted countryside, fairies and leprechauns are part of its inheritance and they are accepted by the old dwellers on the soil who know that they, old as they are, are but as newcomers compared with the Shee, the Good People, the Fairy Folk. The sceptical questions of city folk are regarded as signs of patronage or of an amused tolerance of foolish superstition, and they are resented. That is why the sophisticated never hear the truth about the Good People, much less see them. The case might be different with a merman. Dweller in the sea as he is, he may not be subject to the same taboo of silence regarding those whose dwellings are in the green hills or the glens. If I approached the fishermen in a friendly way without any sign of scepticism or too much curiosity, I might hear "something to my advantage," as the lawyers put it when advertising for lost heirs. I am a lost heir, I thought, lost by too much traffic with townsfolk and hectic civilization, lost to the supernatural and mysterious heritage of my ancient country. Christmas may help me, I hoped, to get the story of the merman from the two who saw him face to face. I was so eager to reach Renvyle that I was a menace to the traffic across country.

Two days elapsed. I resented this waste of time but it would never do to rush things in a part of the country where life moved in a dignified and leisurely gait. It would be better to wait till Christmas Eve when an invitation would not seem to be too intentional. On Christmas Eve I sent a boy "back" to where the fishermen lived. "Back" means any place further to the West than where you happen to live. In this case it was back of Letter Mountain where that mass falls down towards the Atlantic in many a cliff and cove. One of these coves was the Cave na Mblan, The Cave of the Women, for legend had it that the naked bodies of two women were found floating in it in the days when the Spanish Armada was wrecked along that inhospitable coast. It was no longer a cave, for Atlantic breakers had long ago shouldered off its roof so that now it lay open to the light of day—such as it was, for its steep sides admitted light only when the sun was sinking in the sea.

The boy came back with the message that the men could not come. After the usual interrogation it appeared that they were not unwilling to come, but one of them could not walk far owing to an old wound in his leg. I took council with my friends as to the advisability of sending a car for the men. To do so might arouse their suspicions and reveal the fact that it was their story rather than their company I was anxious to have. There was nothing for it but to send the car. We might invite a few of the neighboring country folk to share whatever Christmas cheer the house provided, so as to take the pointedness out of the invitation to those whose enchanted eyes beheld the Merman.

The Guinness had been tapped and the fiddler was tuning up when the fishermen arrived. There was no need to have sent for neighbors, for the fishermen brought, or found themselves saddled with, a "witness," that is a "producer" who battens on anything unusual that happens in the countryside. He need not have "witnessed" anything. He probably got his name from the assistance he or his sort gave to countrymen whose want of knowledge of English handicapped them in an English-speaking court.

It may have been diplomatic to have given to fishermen a few bottles before approaching the real subject of my interest; but with the witness there was no need for such precaution: his tongue was only too loose. In a way he was useful, for, at what he judged to be the appropriate moment, he started his men. First he addressed himself to me.

"Wouldn't you like to hear about a queer thing Pat and Robert here seen two months ago before the winter storms came on?"

"What was the 'queer thing'?" I asked without any show of eagerness.

"Will I tell him, boys?" the "witness" asked his men.

Whether he intended it or not—for he was a subtle rogue, the "witness's" version had the effect of rousing one of the fishermen, Robert Wallace, to intervene.

The Merriman

"You haven't got it quite right," he told the "witness."

"What way was it then?" the "witness" inquired with an injured air. And this is what Robert Wallace said.

"John and I were rowing back with the boat low in the water for it was full of wet nets and fish. We were rounding the point of the Curragh when we saw what we thought was a windfall."

A "windfall" means one of those large glass containers that hold hundreds of gallons of sulphuric acid which was used by the submarines during the first World War. They are protected by a lattice of wicker which surrounds the upper part with a diamond-shaped pattern of osier wood.

"It was floating in the Cave na Mblan. We took the boat in to have a closer look at it. When we next looked over our shoulders, we thought it was a sheep."

"What distance were you from it?" I asked.

He looked at his companion, said something in Irish. His companion nodded. He turned and said, "About a hundred yards."

I was glad that he had consulted his companion for it showed that the men were in agreement.

"Was the sea calm?"

"Very calm."

"What did you do then?"

"We rowed up to it. Then we saw it was a man standing with his waist out of the water. He had blue eyes, and a forehead that went up like that." He threw his hands up beside his head to indicate a forehead that sloped sharply. "He had hair and eye-brows the color of hay." Here there

· 163 ·

was a pause. The man hesitated, looked at his friend, but did not speak.

"Well," I said, "what did you do next?"

The question did nothing to relieve the confusion. Then the "witness" prompted, "Tell the doctor what did yese do then."

"How close were you to it?" I asked to relieve the tension.

Heanue answered this time. "We were that close that we could have leant out and put our hands under his armpits and pulled him into the boat."

"Why didn't you?" I enquired with rising excitement. Dead silence and more confusion this time. Even the witness could not get a word out of them. At last he became peremptory. "Tell the doctor why ye didn't." Slowly and with much reluctance Heanue said, "He might have put a spell upon us."

"Ah!" I said to myself. "This is the first sign that they recognized the presence of the supernatural. That cannot be an invention. It is circumstantial truth."

It was time to open a few more bottles of Guinness; they might ease the situation. But Heanue volunteered to continue the tale.

"As we looked at him he put his arms across his face and sank down into the water with a kind of moaning sound."

"What kind of sound?"

And Heanue made a sound like a man puffing out his breath to make a groan with his lips and not his throat.

I sat silent. Surely this was not made up. Mermen were

scarce and did not share the invention of the country imagination.

"Had he any clothes?"

Wallace said briskly that now they had gotten over the embarrassment of acknowledging fear in the presence of the unknown.

"Over his shoulders he had a thing on him like a half-opened net."

Good, I thought. That bears out their mistaking him for a "windfall" at a distance. The diamond-shaped wicker work "like a half-opened net."

"Was he standing on a rock?"

"Oh, no. There was eight feet of water under him. We looked down and saw that he had a kind of red mark on the front of each foot."

"Was he naked?" I enquired.

"No. He had a kind of little blue kilt."

"Well, go on. What happened? Was that the end of him?"

"No, sir," Wallace said. "He began to follow the boat. We rowed hard but she was heavy and there was a time when he came up to the thwart. He followed us for three hundred yards or so and we were glad to get away from him."

They regarded each other and agreed.

"Did he swim like this," I asked, making a suggestion of the crawl stroke.

"No," they both said at once, "he went under the water like this," and they wavered their hands sideways to suggest an undulating motion.

That was all they told me, but the "witness" had to have his say.

"About twenty years ago, Mr. Blake was out in his yacht and he saw one not very far from the Cave na Mblan. He took up his rifle to shoot it when the men threatened to mutiny on the boat." And the "witness" could not be silenced until he emptied his head of all the legends that dealt with mermen and human brides along the coast as far as Schill Island.

So I dismissed them all with the resolve that if the weather was suitable, I myself would go "back" and have a further talk with the fishermen and inspect the Cave na Mblan.

One windy morning when the bog was dry I walked up the mountain side with a friend, Frank Owen, Editor of *The Evening Standard*, to call on Heanue and Wallace. We learned that they were veterans of World War I, and the man with the wounded leg had lain for six weeks in St. George's Hospital, London. This does not necessarily make a man veracious, but at least it gave him an opportunity to look around and learn not to be a victim of hallucinations. The English are the least fey people on earth. The other man, Wallace, had served with the engineers, a highly intelligent corps of officers and men. In spite of their travels over part of the globe, the call of freedom and the sea and the simple health of carefree Connemara drew them home.

The Cave of the Women was truly a repellent place. Far down, the green Atlantic washed cold between sunless cliffy sides stained yellow in spots with lichens and moulds that grew without any sun. The brownish green cliffs on either side were only slightly slanted. And that was at the top where the roof had fallen in three hundred years ago. Truly the Merman must have had a constitution that could resist the cold, I thought.

We inquired of the fishermen why was he not "called "Fir na Mara" which is the Gaelic for "Man of the Sea." They laughed at me. "That's only schoolmasters' Gaelic," they said. A remark which showed the contempt in which native speakers of the oldest tongue in Europe regard the mischievous attempt to lard the language with *Ersatz* and English words.

"What should he be called?" we inquired. Whereupon they intoned a sound so beautiful and so full of overtones of sweet and fleeting inflections, musical all through like the string of a harp, that my ear could not catch them. It was full of little sounds for which we have neither ear nor organ. English has twenty-six letters in its alphabet, some of them redundant, and probably not one hundred sounds: who are they, for whom such a pedestrian language sufficed to growl their matter-of-fact statements at each other, to set the limits of the possible to men to whom a Merriman was as acceptable as a god to Homer's men? As far as I could make out, it was half way between a word that sounded like "Murriman" and "Merriman," nearer, if anything, to the latter word. One thing was obvious—the apparition was no new thing. There was a name for it in Gaelic on the Connemara coast.

When I got back to Dublin after a few weeks in the country by the side of the ocean from which the Merriman rose, I recounted the whole story to Yeats, who loved to hear of such unaccountable things. He listened with rapt attention. When I finished, I, being too much city bred, began to excuse the interest I had evinced in the story by the suggestion that the thing might have been a dugong which is a mammalian, a dugong lured by the Gulf Stream to leave its natural habitat. This infuriated the poet.

"I am amazed at you," he almost shouted. "Why will people (even you) insist on reducing everything under Heaven to narrow reason's scope? There is enough evidence in the testimony of those decent fishermen whom you could not make contradict themselves to hang a man if it were a case of murder and not of something that visits us rarely, which they were not ready to accept. Why? Because we have beggared our minds of everything that cannot be explained by reason: we who cannot explain our own existence on this planet must explain the existence of everything else."

So subdued was I by this harangue that I resolved from that day to this not to try to explain the inexplicable. After all, there are more things in heaven and earth and sea, especially the sea, than are dreamt of in our philosophies. There are things that come out of the sea, the first of their kind, uncatalogued and unique. And we live only on the fringe of the sea.

Miss Cotton who had an aquarium on Palm Beach one day found a strange creature of the shore. It was about five inches long, scaleless and rubbery, with a little head like a bewhiskered Scotch terrier. Beneath it was a fin-like filament like the wings of a butterfly which it could fold over its back like a cloak. It lived only for two days but during that time she made drawings of it which she showed to that great naturalist, Dr. William Beebe, who remarked that there was no telling in the world what was in the sea. He did not seem surprised by the story of this unique creature. Unprecedented discoveries are occurring every day. In Scotland some years ago the appearance of a sea monster in Loch Ness caused quite a stir amongst the columnists. It was seen at two places at once, so they scoffed. It never occurred to them that there was a school of such sea creatures disporting themselves in that long and very deep ocean inlet called Loch Ness. I saw on the coast of Wales an unknown species that was represented by a large walrus-like mammal, three times the size of any walrus ever seen. It was covered with dark red hair like a mammoth. It had a proboscis instead of tusks. Its fore legs were not flappers but short limbs with claws like an alligator. In length it must have measured twenty-five or twenty-eight feet. I could not measure it accurately for its tail was sunk in the sand.

Yes, as Dr. Beebe said, there are many things in the sea which . . . But here I am relapsing into a welter of rationalism again. Let me not draw the Merriman into this, but leave him to the poet and to kindly fishermen who knew better than to try to lift him from his element.

The Vicarious Fulfillment
of the Vicar of Dumbleton Center

I

Few THINK OF THE UNITED
States of America as the home of simplicity and peace.
This is due to the fact that city life, with its congestion,
complications and distortions, gives more scope to those
who present America to the world than does country life,
with its uneventful routine.

Yet there are many parts of America that are as quiet
and as simple as the oldest rural communities of Europe.
In Maryland, for instance, in some villages the inhabitants go to bed at sundown to save electric light and work
steadfastly in the fields all day. In Vermont where life
is hard and long, contentment reigns unbroken except in
the districts to which retired brokers and business men
have been attracted because of the healthy climate and the
longer expectation of life.

Dumbleton Center is a hamlet just large enough to
support a church. The little Center stands on a flat-topped
knoll from which four roads radiate past houses set in
orchard lawns, and run on through meadows and rich
pastures across brooks and bowery hollows to meet the far
distant "routes" that lead to or from the pleasant coun-

try town at the confluence of the Connecticut and West Rivers.

Daily men went to work and children were collected for school in a bright yellow bus, in the afternoon to be returned by it to their homes. The older ones played games in a triangular field in front of the church, which stood white and square, surmounted by a tower that held a big bell. There appeared to be half a dozen children to each house, which goes to show how prolific was the air of Dumbleton Center.

The younger children played games which were not so pleasant for a stranger or casual passer-by who was liable to be met, in the proper season, by a shower of green apples, the result of the abundant first fall before the fruit grows to maturity. They threw none at their pastor in his daily walk, though that good man would not have grudged the children—Bless their little hearts—what was literally their fling. "Robin, Edgar, Lenny, Marylyn." He knew them all. He had baptized them. But he did not stop to interrupt their games, for he was well aware that all children feel constraint in the presence of authority. He also knew that children can praise the Lord by play, so he let them be. Their parents welcomed him on his daily round. Would he not come in for a moment? But rather than enter he stood and talked. He knew that his presence in a cottage might be a visitation. He took the will for the deed and continued on his walk contented to know that the village lived and moved in the Lord. May God maintain its innocence and keep afar the disquiets and the ambitions that make a people restless to no good end.

Those of his parishioners who had gone to New York and succeeded, paid by absence from the country for their success. Relatively they would have been just as rich had they never left Dumbleton, and more content. Now they used the houses where they were born as "summer homes" and made their center in the modern Babylon where every man was an antagonist to his neighbor and the ends of the earth sent their cunning ones to compete. It was hard to hold to one's integrity in an enormous town. He who goes to Rome must do as the Romans do and what did that mean when applied to New York? It meant, first of all, that a man had to live and move in a lack of space, resign himself to an absence of a home and consequently a lack of family. The best brains of the nation were being sterilized in the towns. And such little space as could be rented between the cliffs of offices, changed hands every year or so. There were no children to throw apples, no apples to be thrown.

He walked on down by the Slab Mill where the dam was broken and the mill-pond filled with flowering waterweeds. The Rev. Jonathan Huckabee felt that a sermon was forming in his mind. He walked past the house of the carpenter, the eccentric who spent his spare time in adding to his house until, to get space, he had to build on around the corner upon piles over the stream. That demented man was dead long since and only half the house was inhabited now. Yes—there was space in the country and romping golden heads.

Other carpenters were busy on a new house. Though the roof was barely finished he saw that the name was painted on the gate posts of the picket fence, "Evenlode." Another "summer home" no doubt. No. The men could not say to whom it belonged. They guessed it was some of those New Yorkers who were buying up half the place and not staying in it. Restless as chipmunks. He did not like to dwell on the loss of integrity and morale by which men and women were threatened in New York because that would be to take an incharitable view of people as a whole; and among the citizens of New York were some of his parishioners. Far be it from him to think ill of them. Yet he could not hide from himself the fact that promiscuity and cuisines were the chief lures of the city and to accept these as a compensation for the household reverences and simple fare of country life argued some change in a man's character. To counteract the lure of the great city he did his best to combat the boredom which is a cause of restlessness and dissatisfaction in the rural scene. He organized evening sing-songs which went the round of one household after another. He got up games and founded a boys' swimming club. In the winter this became a skating and ice hockey club. He tried to change the taste of his flock for vulgar radio programmes. It was hard to find a substitute. He could not find it in music, for music, like every other art had become hackneyed and debauched by those who "presented" it on the air. Comic strips for the children he discouraged but not with much success. The grown-ups he found were addicted to them; but he did point out the fallacy of teaching anything through this medium because (and what loss could be greater) the mind lost the discipline of study and half the advantage of study is the hard way by which learning is acquired. From where he began to climb the hill on his return, the church seemed askew. This was doubtless an optical illusion due to the contour of the hill.

His wife did her best to help her husband. She was much younger and suited to parish work; for she loved children, and this all the more since God had not seen fit to bless her with a progeny of her own. Resigned to God's will she organized jumble sales and took the children round with her to run into the outlying houses and carry off from the woman of the house such objects as she could well spare. She sang when invited at evening concerts but left early to avoid any constraint her presence might impose on the merry meeting. She called on the summer visitors and made friends with those who had come to make their homes permanently in or near the parish. Already she knew three very nice people, a Mr. and Mrs. Furnival Wrigley, a Mr. and Mrs. Konstad Hornby and the wife of an important broker, Mrs. Bennie Reeves whose husband could get away from the city on alternate weekends only. The Reeves were building a much larger house than the one they had rented while "looking round." She felt that she had done much to hasten their decision to reside in the salubrious village of Dumbleton. With the two first named ladies she was diffident and by no means at ease. Yet she felt it her duty to visit them and to invite them to the Vicarage to meet the Vicar. With Mrs. Reeves it was quite different. She was easy to get on with, she was so,—she was about to say "familiar" but that would sound somewhat deprecatory when applied to such a friendly woman as Mrs. Reeves—"confiding" is the better word. She might have been thought "loud" by the distant and superior Mrs. Wrigley or "pushing" by Mrs. Hornby, who was a rather demure woman. To all appearances Mrs. Reeves was far the most affluent of the three. She wondered what her husband was like. It was he who was building "EVENLODE."

One thing she had in common with Mrs. Reeves and that was love of children. Mrs. Reeves adored children and almost wept, so deep was her pathos when she thought not only of her own deprivation but of that of her husband in their childlessness. It was almost tragic and it would have been completely so were it not for the compensating fact that it made him throw himself into money-making with greater avidity. "Just to distract himself," explained Mrs. Reeves. "I hope that we'll have better luck in Dumbleton Center." Which remark Mrs. Huckabee took to be a reference to the possibility of having a child.

Hardly a month had elapsed when Mrs. Reeves confided to the Vicar's wife that she had had it from a most authoritative source that the other two ladies were "no better than myself when it comes to a show-down." Which, being interpreted, meant that Mrs. Reeves had discovered through kitchen channels that the other two ladies had come to reside at Dumbleton with precisely the same hope as her own. It was a striking bit of news that she refrained, however, from telling to her husband for fear of reminding him of his and her own deprivation which would be made all the more poignant if he were to consider that not even Dumbleton could bring an answer to their prayers. It certainly was a revelation. She would never have thought of it had it not been for her friend, the chatty and observant Mrs. Reeves. Now of course, it was quite plain. Neither Mrs. Wrigley or Mrs. Hornby were blessed with offspring. Mrs. Reeves could not be quite sure; but she somehow imagined that Mrs. Wrigley who had married at sixteen had had issue by her first husband. But where that husband was or where his child or children were, she had no means of knowing "just yet."

Mrs. Reeves had "been places" so much that through her Mrs. Huckabee could go on a round-the-world tour vicariously. She was confiding, open and friendly with a rough forthrightness that passed for honesty. At the risk of favoring one parishioner more than another, Mrs. Huckabee was attached to her because of the strange fascination of her outspokenness.

"I'd never have guessed that you were twenty-eight if I hadn't heard it from your own lips. You're only a year older than me."

"I'll be twenty-nine in October," said Mrs. Huckabee resolutely.

"Let me see. Would that be under Virgo or Libra?"

"I cannot say. My husband disapproves of astrology."

"So he would. So does every parson. They're afraid that it would put them out of business. It would be just too bad if you were under Virgo. Libra, and you'd be balanced all right. But up in a place like this, it doesn't matter under what sign you were born. I cannot for the life of me imagine what a good looker like you is doing up here. Church work!" She laughed deridingly.

This was the side of Mrs. Reeves' character, the irreverent side, which jarred on Mrs. Huckabee. There was another side which betrayed an incredible want of any moral principles, scruples or loyalties in regard to sexual relations, while in absurd conjunction with these deficiencies was an illogical parade of "Truth."

"Very well, if he suspects me, I'll tell him the truth and, if he can't take it, to hell with any man who can't stand the truth!"

When Mrs. Huckabee regained her reasoning power she replied with what might be taken for a parable, seeing that argument was useless while the "undivided middle," the defiant word "truth" was unresolved.

"If a man committed murder and told the truth to the Law and was executed, would he have a grievance against the Law for not being able to take the truth?"

"St. Paul to the Corinthians, chapter two," Mrs. Reeves replied with an imitation of clerical intonation.

Truly, Mrs. Reeves was an enigma to Mrs. Huckabee. She was totally amoral. As amoral as any four year old child. She could not be judged by any of the principles of decency by which Mrs. Huckabee had been taught to abide. It is hard to judge people if you cannot tell to what standards they conform. Mrs. Reeves appeared to have none except her preposterous "Truth." Was she one of the new emancipated women who thought that there was nothing that could not be solved by "intellect." A very convenient doctrine for those who repudiated any sense of guilt or sin. To them Mrs. Huckabee would be "Victorian," which implied that to cling fast to that which is good was a stupid survival of Puritanism. It was "stuffy" to object to unlimited licentiousness. There was nothing illicit to Mrs. Reeves, not even her husband's philandering. "I am promiscuous," Mrs. Reeves boasted; "and if he is promiscuous, I can beat him to it any day,"—as if there was no such thing as lasting love. Loyalty and honor meant nothing to her. She said, and it was not said as a confession but just a casual statement that during the time she was devoted to a professor of biology, she was "trying it out" with her present husband.

"You don't think that I'd marry a man without finding out beforehand whether he was potent or not."

Treachery she did not even sense. She was as promiscuous as a city punk. Shocking, but there it was. She was so different from Mrs. Huckabee that she went without blame, as an animal goes without blame for being neither modest nor ashamed.

The shocked look on Mrs. Huckabee's face was interpreted according to Mrs. Reeves' notions of propriety.

"Oh he was good enough then, but now I'm beginning to have my doubts."

"But why do you want children at all?" gasped Mrs. Huckabee.

"Because I'm damned if I'll adopt a foundling just to please Bennie and 'keep me quiet,' as he says."

She was amoral, so amoral that Mrs. Huckabee decided that it would be inadvisable to report the conversation to her husband, as she felt in duty bound. It would only pain him. He might think it his duty to approach Mr. Reeves and expostulate with him—one bad apple can rot the whole lot—how far that would go and how it would end she could not foresee. If any serious incident should arise, she would have herself to blame and nobody respects a gossip or a tell-tale.

Dumbleton Center was filling up with summer visitors. School mistresses, tired stenographers, a few couples waiting for divorces, half a hundred old people unable to sustain a summer in New York, a medical student or two, and, what caused much surmise, a well-known lady doctor who apparently was in attendance on Mr. and Mrs. Hornby. She was staying at their house and when Mrs. Huckabee went to invite them to her "at home" she included Dr. Marion Dalyrumple in the invitation. The doctor was delighted to accept, for she had taken a liking at first sight to the rector's young wife.

Yes, Dumbleton Center was filling up. You got ocular proof of it on Sunday at church when the Rev. Jonathan Huckabee preached to a full congregation. A congregation that would have been fuller had Mrs. Reeves not "preferred a pillow to a pew." The seldom-seen Mr. Reeves was there. To curiosity more than to devotion this may have been due. His only association with religion was his tie, which outshone the stained-glass windows. As a rule the Vicar preached to his rustic audience so that his words held interest for them all. In summer when the church was filled with strangers he preached on a more universal theme. So it was to-day.

You would say to see him that, for all his gentleness and loving kindness he looked a magnificent specimen of a man, upright in body as well as in mind, and of a fearless and dignified mien.

His appearance in the pulpit filled the visitors from New York with admiration and respect which they passed on to his holy office. He made little reference to Holy Writ except for one quotation and his text which he took from St. Paul's letter to the Hebrews.

> *"Marriage is honorable in all, and the bed undefiled, but whoremongers and adulterers God will judge."*

He spoke without a hint of the official drone, but in a kindly and sonorous voice.

"Friends and brothers, we have been led by God's guidance through darkness and devastation back by the red path of Victory to Peace. Millions of our countrymen and allies have lost their lives, many have lost their loved ones whom they held dearer than their lives. Cities have been razed, whole countries de-populated, and nations that have contributed much to mankind have been thinned almost to extinction.

"The Spirit of Evil which brought the human race to fratricidal war has not wholly vanished from the earth. He stalks the land, the land afar and the land of home. Afar off, Friends, he is fostering an ill will to revenge and negating all attempts at amelioration by infusing men's hearts with hate. Ideologies of evil he has invented, and caused those who hold such ideas to look upon us with suspicion. Envy and hatred and covetousness are abroad over more than one sixth of the surface of the earth. Not only our civilization but our existence is being threatened, not by the force of arms or the supremacy of the intellect, but by the weight of multitudes. The American Race for all its wealth and armament is not only not immune from this threat but is contributing to its own extinction. Americans are withholding from the Nation the gift of life. Men are refusing to be fathers and women shrink from maternity for their own reasons which are opposed not only to the welfare of the entire People but to the will of God. You have heard the command 'Increase and multiply.' What is the answer? I hold it in my hand."

Here the Rev. Mr. Huckabee produced *The Reader's Digest* and read an article on abortion and birth control. "The amount of money expended in one year on contraceptive apparatus fills me with awe and horror. The figures are incredible. They lead one to imagine that out of every million possible pregnancies, conception takes place in fewer than a fraction of 1 per cent.

"I will not read further. I will explain what this means.

"You have heard the Devil, or the Spirit of Evil defined as 'The Spirit who denies.' He who denies his wife and his nation the most significant and precious thing in the world which is life, he is turning himself verily into a devil and forwarding the Devil's work. This is the Supreme Sin, the Sin against the Holy Ghost, the *Logos Spermaticos* which is the Creator of all.

"Friends, let me desist from using what to you may be hackneyed terms, words too often taken in vain and abused. Let me not say 'Devil' or talk of 'sin.' Let me use the language with which we are all familiar, the language of the work-a-day world, the language of statistics or even of the Stock Exchange and ask ourselves what all this means. What does it mean when parents who are capable refuse to bring children into the world. It means that they are saying to the whole world: life in the United States can be worked out very well for a couple provided they don't encumber themselves with kids. That means that life here is all very well for us, but it is not fit for the next generation. Is this Civilization's answer to the menace of the Eastern hordes? If this be so, it would be better to take in hand a ceremonial dagger such as the nobles of Japan use to commit suicide than to employ any of the contrivances which are mentioned in this magazine."

Again he raised *The Reader's Digest* for all to see.

"To those who say 'Damn America. It will never see a son or a daughter of mine,' I have more to say.

"When I was a young man just about to enter Holy Orders, I asked myself would not the best contribution I could make to my fellow men be to work among them where they are in danger of being dehumanized by the slums of great cities? Then I thought that it would be better to try to hold those who were on the land and happy amid rural surroundings, to hold them away from the congestion of cities, the confinement of tenements and the sterilizing and suicidal effect of the lack of space on man and woman. That is why I am here and devoted to country life.

"This is a happy place. You may see for yourselves the glow of health on the faces of the young and the vigor and longevity of the old. Children play in the ample gardens and go to school not from cellars but from the smiling countryside.

"This is to me America and not an oriental bazaar. To this fruitfulness the city dweller either cannot or will not contribute. To those who will not, I say, you are worse than our deadliest enemy for you deny life forever, while death can but take that which already has lived. As I promised, I will not urge my argument by the use of clerical terms, but (and believe me there is no very great contrast)," here he smiled, "in the language of common sense."

"Marriage is honorable in all. It is a proud thing to be a parent. It is, as the poet said, 'The true pathos and sublime of human life.' Love is the greatest gift God can bestow on us: to love and to have your love multiplied on this earth and when you die to have the innocent prayers of your children follow you on angel wings to Heaven.

"Set your faces against the denial of our noble land. Set your faces against race suicide. Do not invite the lowest species of the human kind to overwhelm this great nation and, by acting as a fifth column, bring it artificially and maliciously into decline.

"Do not say 'Nay' to America. Rather say with the prophet,

> "Rejoice, thou barren that bearest not:
> Break forth and cry thou that travailest not."

He omitted the rest of the sentence, perhaps in accordance with his promise not to inflict his varied audience with church phraseology.

The Vicar of Dumbleton Center

After the sermon, there were visitors to the vestry to congratulate the preacher. Dr. Marion Dalyrumple was the first to express her appreciation. "May I say, Reverend, that I whole-heartedly agree with you. You have touched a chord in my heart that is more than responsive." The Vicar scrutinized his visitor who was of "canonical age," that is, of an age when, had she belonged to the Church of Rome, youth is no longer an obstacle to becoming a priest's housekeeper. But her next statement reassured whatever quaint surmises were forming in his mind. "It may interest you to know that I have devoted my life to the study of fecundity. I am an M.D. and a member of the National Research Foundation for the alleviation of sterility. Your sermon was well-timed and heartening."

The Vicar looked thoughtful and it was reflected in his eyes as he gazed at the eager lady doctor. He was about to ask if she would give his wife and him the pleasure of her company to dinner some evening, when Mr. Hornby slapped him gently on the back. On the Vicar's turning round, Mr. Hornby smiled and said "fine." Mr. Wrigley reached the vestry alone because his wife objected to a sermon that, for all its good intentions, permitted sex to invade the church.

To the lady doctor Bennie Reeves spoke and not to the Vicar.

"I'd like to have a word with you, Doctor, when you can find it convenient. I heard you telling the reverend what you specialize in."

Dr. Dalyrumple's cold stare was lost on the exuberant Mr. Bennie Reeves.

"If you wish to consult me, let me have your card."

When Mr. Reeves produced his card he held it for a moment and admonished it, "There now, be nice to the doctor and remind her that we have a professional engagement next week when we will make it our business to get together when we get back from New York. There now! Expense is no objection. Here you are, Doctor. Quiet please."

The facetious Mr. Reeves left the vestry smiling. He cast a greedy eye on the vicar's wife, who was entering by the side door. He dropped his hat and, while picking it up, he heard Mrs. Huckabee invite Dr. Dalyrumple to dine at the vicarage. He wished now that he had ingratiated himself with the vicar before talking to the doctor. He never had much luck in a church.

II

"Eleanor," the vicar said after dinner, "will you excuse me if I ask Dr. Dalyrumple to speak to me in my study? We will re-join you in a little while."

"Of course. Of course." And the vicar opened the door and directed Dr. Dalyrumple into his book-lined room.

"Pray be seated." When the doctor took a chair, the vicar said, "Doctor, your remark as to the subject of your study interested me profoundly. For a moment I thought that it was to prenatal care you were referring until you mentioned the word 'fecundity.' The vestry was hardly the place for further elucidation, crowded as it was with my parishioners. But I feel that as a pastor I should keep myself acquainted with the advance of science, particularly in such a vital subject as children, who are the foundation around which the family, the unit of our civilization, is built. There is, too, a more intimate reason for asking for your help for which I must of course put myself on the footing of one who comes to consult you professionally. Mrs. Huckabee and I are unblessed by offspring and, apart from any feelings of my own, consideration for Mrs. Huckabee would constrain me to seek advice. I may state for your own information that we have consulted specialists before this and all have concurred in their opinion that there was no physical reason, if I may put it in that way, why we cannot have children like ordinary folk. Is there anything that the medical fraternity has discovered recently?"

The doctor looked at the empty grate instead of looking directly at the vicar, who had betrayed some embarrassment while he was speaking. She said, "Our foundation has certainly made strides. Apart from the RH factor, which is a blood grouping recently discovered that makes for incompatibility, there is the most important discovery of artificial insemination.

"We have advanced far in this research, but considerable work still must be done before we arrive at a technique that can be made adaptable to every case. However, we have catalogued the chief causes of failure, which are—"

She glanced at the vicar, who was following her with rapt attention.

"Which are, failure from lack of perseverance; failure of the woman to cooperate; and misguided selection of male donors. The mistake is usually selection of a male relative for sentimental reasons. A donor of high fertility should be selected."

"Donor?" the vicar murmured audibly.

Dr. Dalyrumple was embarrassed by the unusual surroundings, the necessary reticences, and the vicar's obvious distress. This was infectious, for the doctor had difficulty in finding words with which to convey to the vicar the meaning of "donor," the indispensability of the man and his functions. She said, "You see, insemination naturally requires a supply of the male element, as you can realize from the derivation of the word. The supplier is called the "donor," just as they who give their blood to the Red Cross are called "donors." The very fact that it is artificial removes every consideration of passion, emotion, or even sentiment. The operation is a strictly scientific one. The woman may even be unaware that she is being treated and, as for the donor, who will in due course become a father, he may remain just as anonymous as, for instance, the giver of a pint of blood."

"Remarkable," the vicar said. "Nevertheless the result is adultery, conscious or unconscious. Unless, of course, insemination were employed as an adjuvant to the marital act."

The doctor refrained from telling her host that the findings were all against a husband as a donor, fearing to hurt his feelings. But she joined issue on the verdict of adultery. "It can hardly be called 'adultery.' A woman has been successfully treated three thousand miles **away** from the donor. That word seems too harsh for such **a** purely scientific achievement."

"Distance cannot condone adultery, I am afraid," the vicar said.

Dr. Dalyrumple asked, "What jury would condemn **as** adulterous a couple who never had met, touched, seen **or** heard one another, and had lived all their lives three thousand miles apart?"

"It certainly is a problem," the vicar conceded. "I am very grateful indeed for your information and if you will have your secretary send me an account of my liability to you, I will be glad to discharge it."

"I will not hear of such a thing," the little doctor said. "I am only too happy to give you any information I possess; for I flatter myself that I am a co-worker with you on the subject of repopulation, if I may put it that way."

"The results of your researches have not been made known to the general public?" the vicar asked.

"Professional etiquette would preclude that. I give advice to my patients only. But unfortunately we cannot prevent the popular magazines from feeding the public on garbled, half-informed, and highly colored reports, which they make up from the papers read before our society."

"My reason for asking," the vicar said, "was because I think I can foresee the grave abuses to which any unethical and unscrupulous group could put this, this discovery. Not to speak of the legal problems to which it might conceivably give rise on the question of legitimacy in cases of inheritance for example. Bastardy and disinheritance could be urged." Dr. Dalyrumple glanced at the vicar when he said "conceivably," but she could detect no attempt at punning or of humor in his attitude toward what, evidently, had affected him gravely. In the silence that followed, she arose and the vicar rose, too, saying, "What will Mrs. Huckabee imagine has delayed us?"

On their return from escorting the doctor to the home of her hosts, the vicar spoke of the interview. He explained to his wife that while of course he could not entertain for a moment the idea of any donor but himself, the advance that science had made in the alleviation of sterility was one that should not be overlooked. They could not expect an answer to their prayers if they omitted any means that might facilitate the will of Providence. While they could not expect a miracle to be wrought in their favor, there was every reason to avail themselves of the new methods by which conception might be wrought and that would be an all-sufficing miracle.

"Is it very painful?" Mrs. Huckabee inquired.

"My dear, I do not know the technical details. I could hardly ask a woman to explain, even though she is an M.D. But even if it is, there is always anaesthesia."

Mrs. Huckabee remained silent. Her eyes were full of tears. At last she said, "I don't mind trying at all."

The rector comforted her. "You are very brave," he said. "For all we know, this notion of pain may be a figment of our imagination. Dr. Dalyrumple said nothing about it. What she did say was that one of the causes of sterility was the woman's failure to cooperate. And, now that I remember, she also said that the woman might even be unaware that she was conceiving. Of course, this could have meant an anaesthetic. I can now inform her when I am seeing her again that there can be no question of the wife's not cooperating in our case."

"Of course not, dear," said Mrs. Huckabee.

III

When Bennie Reeves returned to the Curb, he at once directed his secretary to get a "scan" on Dr. Marion Dalyrumple. This revealed that the lady's position in her bank was "substantial." She had read a paper not three months ago, before a gynecological society, which had caused considerable discussion both from the scientific standpoint and the standpoint of jurisprudence. The problems to which it could give rise were discussed from their scientific and social aspects, problems that would entail alterations in the law, common and ecclesiastical. But from the latter point of view no objections were raised by the members of that learned society.

"Get me a copy right away," Bennie Reeves commanded.

One morning when the vicar was about to go on his walk, three little children called at the vicarage to ask if they might gather the fallen apples and take them "back to Daddy's piggy wigs?" New England farmers let nothing go to waste.

When the vicar had raked the August fall together, he

helped the children to fill their baskets and to carry off the green globes. He then set out.

Mrs. Reeves was swinging gently in a hammock as the vicar pushed open the door of the garden gate. From where he stood, he could see that she was sun-bathing. And though it cannot be said that one is busily engaged sun-bathing, there were other reasons for which the rector refrained from disturbing her.

A revolving spray at either end of the hammock rainbowed the light. Behind, a wall of rambler roses screened the hammock from the wind. Mrs. Reeves waved a shapely arm the skin of which was veinless and dull white. The sun had made her shoulders the color of smoked salmon, and as tender.

"Try the front door," called Mrs. Reeves.

By the time the vicar had stepped up to the veranda the door was opened by Mrs. Reeves who was now clothed becomingly in a bathrobe patterned with birds in flight and flowers in bloom.

"Won't you come in?" said Mrs. Reeves.

To this invitation the vicar replied rather hesitatingly with a resigned, "Ah, well." As he entered the hall, he said, "I thought that as I was passing I would drop in to make myself acquainted with Mr. Reeves. He left before I could get to him in the vestry last Sunday."

"So he went to church?" Mrs. Reeves inquired. "Can you beat that? Curiosity killed the cat."

She measured the vicar with drenched brown eyes as liquid as those of people who are accustomed to wearing glasses and have just removed them.

"Would you care for a drink? There is everything. You can have anything you want." Demurely she cast down her eyes and watched a gently moving, crimson-tipped toe.

"Not at all. Not at all," the vicar said. "I dropped in to make your husband's acquaintance—and yours."

"Thank you for including me. But Bennie's down in New York and he may not be back until the weekend after this. Unless, that is to say, he has found something to interest him in church."

"I sincerely hope he has," the vicar said. "I like Dumbleton's summer visitors to come to church."

"What's this about summer visitors. We're here for keeps. 'Evenlode' is going to be our teepee. And I'll love it. I'll say I will."

"You will, of course," the vicar concurred.

"I will like——. I warned Bennie that as soon as I recover, I'll go back to New York, and no more prenatal care for me."

"Prenatal care?" the vicar repeated.

"Yes; prenatal: I am supposed to get pregnant up here in this blooming healthy place of yours. Good air, rest, and balanced diets, and . . . what have you?"

"The air is certainly invigorating," the vicar agreed, "owing, no doubt, to the seasonal contrasts between heat and cold. If you would care to read it, I can lend you a book on the climate of Vermont. . . ."

"Me? Books?" Mrs. Reeves said with what seemed revulsion at the thought. "There isn't a darned thing I don't know about books. I was a reviewer until I met Bennie, who was interested in a chain of book stores at the time. I hated the sight of a book outside business hours. And, talking of climate, have you read Huntington's book on the increasing aridity of the subtropic zone?"

"I can't say I have," the vicar confessed.

"Well, get it. It explains how what used to be the granary of Rome, North Africa, dried up; why Zenophon's Ten Thousand could never have made it but for oases which have disappeared since; and it tells why southern cities make men effete and tend to become decadent themselves. Do you know why? You would never guess: this weakness is due to the receding of the polar ice. When north of Sweden it melts, the center of the earth dries up. Then comes the turn of the northern climes. They invigorate you. Don't tell me. That's why, when Bennie read it, he parked me up here. There'd be a lot to be said for Vermont if it had more inhabitants—it's lonesome for strangers like me." Her face puckered itself up like a baby's as she questioned his with her liquid eyes. Finding more puzzlement than sympathy in the vicar's look, she pouted and turned her eyes away.

The vicar was certainly puzzled: here was a young woman who could review books and give an intelligent account of them and yet did not trouble to avoid the vernacular when she spoke. She had by sheer intelligence, come up "the hard way." Obviously she represented one of the cases that illustrated the early influence of the home. Were he to lend her one of his many books on the subject of child psychology and the influence of the home, she might take it amiss. No; she had surrounded herself with a rind to immunize herself from the slings and arrows of the work-a-day world. She had separated her emotions from the subject of her study just as a dealer in works of art cannot afford to admire them for anything but their commercial appeal.

The tinkle of glasses aroused the vicar.

"Are you quite sure I can offer you nothing?" asked Mrs. Reeves.

IV

Bennie was back! He had not been expected by anyone. His tie announced his arrival at the railway station and sent out heliographic messages from the gradually rising ground by the river right up to his house where he was not met at the door by his non-expectant wife. She was lolling on a *chaise longue* toying with *Esquire* and *The New Yorker*. Other magazines that took a less serious view of life lay strewn upon the floor.

When she caught sight of him, she warned Bennie who was about to embrace her, not to touch her shoulder, which was still tender from the sun.

"Ho now! Ho now!" thought Bennie. "Who's her latest. She hasn't lost much time." He interpreted the sign of repugnance by the light of long experience. However, he obeyed and contented himself by saluting her where the make-up would be least disturbed, which was the back of her hand. Then, having called her a few dutiful and endearing names, he said, "I have something to show you, kid."

He waved the paper that Dr. Dalyrumple had read before the medical group in New York.

"What is it?" she asked languidly. "You know that I cannot read without my glasses."

Though there was an inventory in each of his bright dark eyes, he apparently did not notice the welter of magazines which she had been reading.

Bennie volunteered, "Here's the report of the Associated Press Science Editor on the remarks of Dr. Dintenfass which goes on to say, 'Dr. Dintenfass further reported that in his experience using the husband as a donor is nearly always a failure.' "

"So he would," she commented.

"There's your out, Baby."

"Out? For me?"

"Sure. The husband is a bad donor."

"You're telling ME. And so what?"

"So what? You can have anyone you like; that is, within scientific limits."

"Better fix yourself a drink."

While her husband was dutifully obeying, she drawled, "May I ask to what I owe the pleasure of your company this weekend?"

"I rushed up to bring you the good news and to keep an appointment with Dr. Dalyrumple who is an expert at the business. Don't I deserve one little kiss?"

"Your expert will probably arrange that, too."

She fanned herself with *The New Yorker* which is a lighter paper than *Esquire*.

Meanwhile, at the home of the Hornbys quite a different conversation was in progress. Dr. Dalyrumple was speaking to Hornby and saying, "As for the vicar becoming a donor, you may put that out of your head. He has the most reactionary ideas about the whole business; but, if you won't take it from me, go to see him yourself."

Hornby said, "Well, there's that; but, after what he preached that Sunday, he must be a bit of a paradox. My wife doesn't like him and for that very reason she wants him for a donor, that is, for the child's sake: an upright and honorable fellow like the vicar. Besides, she says it would hurt my feelings less if the donor were a clergyman and one for whom she had no particular regard. And I think that what she says is right. If we had him for donor, it would give us a clue beforehand as to the character we might expect the child to have, a thing there's no way of foretelling in the case of an adopted child."

"You have just mentioned one of the principal reasons why I feel myself entitled to recommend insemination to those who plan to adopt a child. It has the advantage of giving a hint as to character and the added advantage that the child will be the offspring of at least one of the parents, which is not the case in adoption."

Mr. Hornby, who was tall, grave, and cadaverous, with a concave furrow on each side of his face, was graver as he approached the vicarage. The vicar was in.

"May I have a word with you, Reverend?"

"Certainly, certainly," the vicar retreated smiling, "Come right in."

Mr. Hornby who wore very personal and fancy waist-coats to give him individuality, as it were, had two strings to his bow that gave him courage to speak to the vicar in person. First, he could say that he came on his wife's be-

half more than on his own. Second, he could remind the
vicar of what he had preached on Sunday and thus put
the onus on his sermon. He would use that as an opening
gambit. He began. "That sermon of yours, Reverend,
made a great impression not only on me but on Mrs.
Hornby who . . ."

The vicar said nervously, "Won't you sit down?"

This almost stopped Mr. Hornby whose poker face
concealed his trepidation. He had to start all over again
and he felt at a disadvantage in a chair.

"Well, Vicar, it's like this," he said, all his rhetoric dis-
persed. "Mrs. Hornby asked me to ask you to be the
donor of her child. She wants, we both want to assure ourselves as far as any such thing is possible that we won't
be raising a dud, so to speak. Do you get me?" He ceased.
The vicar's breath could be heard returning. At last he
spoke.

"Little did I think that any Christian could possibly be
misled by a discovery however modern, from the standards
of morality, which are fixed and do not change. Science
is no substitute for morality. I know that you are unaware
of the true character of your proposal, as you obviously
are unaware of how revolting it seems to me. That is why
I do not regard it as an insult, particularly as I represent
religion in this parish."

"But you said, 'he who denies another, his wife or his
nation the most precious thing which is life, is acting the
devil's part,' or words to that effect. It seems to me that
you are denying life to my wife and we are lawfully married folk. I told you that I am here because of your
sermon."

The vicar bowed his head, "Gracious heaven," he sighed, "Can anyone be more misinterpreted?"

Then seeing the injured look on his visitor's face, he tried to put his position in a light that would convince Mr. Hornby and, of course, Mrs. Hornby of the enormity of their proposal.

"Let me make myself clear. For my own wife I have not the least objection to the efforts of Dr. Dalyrumple to consummate the natural reproductive act on my part; but it is quite another thing to fertilize another man's wife with the male element of one who is not her husband. I do trust that there is no misconception, that is, no mistake as to my attitude in this new-fangled and dangerous discovery."

"Well, I suppose I have got you. I hope, Reverend, that there is no ill feeling." He extended his hand.

V

"What did I tell you?" Dr. Dalyrumple asked as she sat at dinner with her hosts, the Hornbys.

"I guess that you were right; but the vicar gave me an idea. He says that he has no objection to your efforts with his wife when he is the donor, but as for another man's wife . . . But is there anything to prevent you from treating the missus there after you visited Mrs. Huckabee? You remember how you pointed out the advantage of the donor being kept in the dark about his parenthood. Get the idea?"

Dr. Dalyrumple considered this proposition not from the ethical but the scientific point of view and the professional point of view. She quickly summed up the pros and cons. The pros were far in the ascendant; and, that being so, it would be diplomatic to begin by urging a con.

"Nothing at all stands in the way of our availing ourselves of that situation, for Nature is superabundant, profusion and waste are her attributes. But there is one very great objection."

"Let's have it," Hornby asked eagerly.

"It is this, and it lies beyond me to control: I can manage everything else, but I cannot protect myself by the secrecy that is indispensable to my work."

"Do you mean that I would tell?" Mrs. Hornby asked. "Do you know that if it weren't for the sake of the child, I would have nothing to do with that reluctant clergyman."

"It's all to the good that he is reluctant. We don't want a donor to know who is raising his child, and if I have to employ the usual donors of strong fertility, they come from a section of the community that would not be as scrupulous as the vicar. So you see the importance of secrecy."

"As far as we are concerned," Hornby said, "we can give you all the assurance that you may require and, what is more, lay aside a sum to be forfeited in the very unlikely event of injury to your professional reputation. Let's go!"

"I may as well tell you that the experiment has to be repeated three times a month, and that involves so many intimacies of family life that those alone would call for secrecy."

"We are all set," said Hornby. The doctor nodded.

"You might telephone to Wrigley," Mrs. Hornby said, "to save him from the vicar. He is going to see him to-night."

VI

Dr. Dalyrumple's interview with Bennie was very different from the arrangement so quietly come by with the Hornbys. It did not take that astute doctor one second to realize that with such a person as Bennie, discretion was out of the question.

There's many a shady transaction that ends in the sun of Miami; but had she conceded to Mr. Reeves' proposals, her operations and the names of all concerned would be the talk of the Curb and, more appropriately, of the Stork Club for weeks.

"I do say it. I refuse absolutely. And I advise you not to put your proposal to the vicar. You would only insult him and find yourself rebuffed."

"Rebuffed! I'm having them all the time. What about the rebuff Mrs. Bennie will give me when I come home with the bad news?"

The doctor went on, "And I will add another objection. I object very much to your showing that paper of mine, which was meant only for the medical profession, to all and sundry."

"All and sundry!" Bennie expostulated. "I never heard of such a thing."

"Even to the plumber who called here and offered himself as a donor any time I wanted one."

"I'll tell that bastard where he gets off. Excuse me, Ma'am. You know what I mean." Had Bennie meant that the plumber would not get off with a bastard or numerous surrogates, his meaning would have been more or less the same.

"I knew the very minute I entered the house that the missus had something new up her sleeve. She refused to let me hug her. That's almost a sure sign. Blamed it on sunburn. I know those sunburns. It only took me till next morning to find out that she has fallen head over heels for the vicar. She can't stop complaining about him. He won't take a drink or a cigarette, doesn't seem to want to be friendly. Then deliberately not going to church so that he would come to ask why. If she doesn't have the vicar, my life will be hell."

"When I see Mrs. Reeves, I will explain that there are other donors not necessarily in Dumbleton Center."

"I know, you can fly them up in a thermos all over the place," her irrepressible client remarked. "She wants the vicar. She asked me to grow a beard."

"I trust you will explain that to your wife," the doctor said tartly. "She is my patient, not you."

With that the interview concluded.

VII

Almost a year had elapsed after his call when the vicar met two children at the vicarage door who asked for green apples for Mrs. Reeves.

"She wants to eat them."

Dear, dear, thought the vicar, whatever does she want to eat green apples for? He asked the children why could she not make use of her own.

"They're sold to the farmers. Mr. Reeves don't like pigs. So Mrs. Reeves ain't got none."

"Has none," the vicar corrected.

"And she said that you would send them if you knew of her condition."

The vicar had become a much mellower man since his wife had had twins. He was also more experienced. Could it be that Mrs. Reeves was pregnant and had one of those aberrations of appetite that women are said to have during pregnancy. Green apples? Yes, obviously.

"Tell Mrs. Reeves that my wife will bring her some apples when she goes out with the perambulator."

And the little tots ran off.

Mrs. Hornby's child was born first, that is to say about three weeks before the vicar's wife had the twin boys. Mrs. Wrigley, who was somewhat older, about ten years older, than Mrs. Hornby, had a baby girl. It was born in New York. To Boston Mrs. Hornby went for her confinement. And that left Mrs. Reeves the only one who did not take the precaution of seeking hospitalization elsewhere.

Before the children returned with the apples from the vicarage, Mrs. Reeves was delivered of a nine pound baby boy.

He was a solemn-eyed little fellow who seldom cried.

"Thank Heaven he doesn't make a fuss like Bennie. He will be christened at the Center and I will call him 'Jonathan.' "

This announcement was made some days later by Mrs. Reeves; and more than ever now, her word was law.

There were three christenings all in one day for there were only a few weeks between the ages of the babies. The vicar's twins had been christened privately by the rector of Newfane.

There was any amount of junketing. The three fathers gave a treat to all the Center. Children sang after church service, which was specially arranged for the occasion. The population of the Center had increased remarkably. Many visitors came from New York and, though some rumors of the three births after varying lengths of sterility were abroad, none reached the press. They were not sufficiently remarkable to be "news"; but they were news enough to the Curb, some members of which came to the Center for vacation on the suggestion, if not the invitation, of Bennie. The vicar gave a short address to those assembled before they should become distracted by games and innocent pastimes.

"Parishioners and Friends" he said. He spoke in the open air in the triangle outside his church. "It gives me the greatest pleasure to address you. This is indeed a happy occasion, both for the parents of the three babies I have christened this morning, and for me and my wife with our bright-eyed twins. I know with what satisfaction they must have seen their offspring made members of our Christian communion, with what satisfaction they saw their friends' offspring, and with what satisfaction they realized that they were parents and members of our friendly little group.

"I regard these new parents as exemplary people because to them is due the reversal for which I have worked these many years, the reversal from the city to the countryside. If substantial people would withdraw from the cities, the cities would cease to be the sterilizing centers of the nation. It is to the presence of substantial men and women that, although they do not realize it, the overcrowding of our cities is due; and due the results of that overcrowding. Providence could not have given us more striking and happy object lessons to prove the truth of my contention. You have seen three babies christened who, I will be bold and say it, could not have been conceived in New York. No. The invigoration gained from this salubrious village of ours is the direct cause of these three births. It is not generally known that there is a process going on on the earth's surface by which towns and territories south of a certain zone and a few parallels of latitude tend to become sterile and to turn into desert regions. When I learned this from a charming member of our community, I accepted it as a parable or rather simile of what goes on in the souls of those who think not of children but only of themselves. Their selfishness makes them arid and they dry up, physically as well as mentally. When I think of this process going on in Nature, I realize with gratitude and joy that Vermont, that New England is slowly but inevitably coming into its own. As the cold weather leaves the torrid zone, countries in that zone tend to dessicate and to disappear. Meanwhile, countries situated farther north increase in fertility and power. That is what we are experiencing in this very Center.

Apart from the direct interference of Providence on the behalf of those new parents, there is the strong earth movement, the retreat of the polar ice (which is also an act of Providence), which renders this Center exceptionally invigorating. Three christenings this morning are all the proofs I will call to establish my point. To Providence then let us render thanks, to Providence which has blessed particularly Dumbleton Center, to Providence, and to the retreat of the polar ice."

Dr. Dalyrumple as before was the first to congratulate the vicar on every count.

When the doctor left the vestry, she walked into Bennie. "Well, well, well," he said.

She was relieved from answering his enigmatical ejaculations by the arrival of a perambulator in which the vicar's twins were fast asleep. Bennie, constrained by a convention to which he with difficulty conformed, bent his head into the perambulator and was about to talk baby-talk when the twins awoke with the nearest approach to a scream that they could make.

"It's a wise child," thought Dr. Dalyrumple.

Nonplussed, Bennie began to disparage the babies. "They look wizened and a bit shrivelled up," he said.

Dr. Dalyrumple's indignation overcame her restraint. "What can you expect when you spare the rod?" she asked; and before the full import of her remark entered Bennie's brain, she was gone.

Reminiscences of Yeats

In A ROOM IN THE OLD-fashioned Nassau Hotel, which looked northward into College Park, Dublin, a group of authors and actors had banded together in the early 1900's to read new plays and to settle by vote which plays should be produced, and where and when. The idea of thus introducing democracy into art was George Russell's. Though it gave the actors, who were all amateurs, an opportunity to meet the playwrights, it also provided the stimulus for arguments that lasted, in some instances, for months. For their productions the group hired cheap halls, such as St. Theresa's Hall in Clarendon Street and a kind of clubhouse in Camden Street, and between rehearsals they held lectures on art and on the drama. So began the literary movement that was later to become the world-famous Abbey Theatre and the Irish National Theatre.

Yeats, Russell (AE), Colum, Synge, Lady Gregory, perhaps Maude Gonne (I say "perhaps" for there was little love lost between the ladies), and the two brothers Fay, Frank and William, were present on one of the rare occasions when I attended a meeting of the Literary Theatre, as the group then called itself. Synge's *Riders to the Sea* had just been read, and was received with grave silence. At last Yeats exclaimed, "Aeschylus!" and inclined his head. Everyone agreed, including the man beside me, who asked in an awe-struck whisper, "Who is Aeschylus?" Ever ready to impart information, even when the readiness outruns accuracy, I replied, "A man who is like Synge."

This is my earliest recollection of meeting Yeats. I often try to remember who it was who introduced us. The probability is that it was the democracy of the occasion that brought us together. No one formally introduced us. We just met.

I had first heard of Yeats from J. E. Healy, an editor of the *Evening Mail*, a somewhat conservative Dublin paper. Healy was a scholar of Trinity College, and his admiration for Yeats's prose impressed me very much. I began to suspect that I was missing something by my devotion to out-door sports. As a matter of fact, I was missing the beginning of what turned out to be the Irish Renaissance. I was missing the poetry of the period and the most important poet of his time. When I at last met Yeats, who looked every inch (and there were seventy-three inches of him) a poet, I wondered why Healy had referred to his prose.

In those days of 1902, Yeats looked exactly like the charcoal drawing John Sargent had made of him. The sketch shows a gaunt, upright young man, with a shock of dark hair falling over the left brow. Sargent had caught a gesture of Yeats's body-making itself. The jaw is clear-cut and firm. The mouth is beautifully modelled. The nose is aquiline, with great breadth between the eyes, one of which—the right—is noticeably lower than the other. Around his long throat is a soft collar and flowing silk tie. Since the drawing is in black and white, it conveys no idea of the complexion of the poet. His cheeks were russet brown, his cheek-bones touched with color. His mouth was remarkable for the translucent lips that were soft and red like the berry of the yew. He had a charming voice with mellow tones that quickened with his thoughts. He was tall and dark and looked mysterious in a mitigated light. There was about him a strange aloofness—a remoteness—and he had a way of withdrawing into himself, the effect of which was as though someone had suddenly turned off a light. His aloofness, however, was probably prompted by shyness, which he threw off only when aroused.

The writers and actors who unknowingly were infusing a soul into Ireland dedicated their time—in some instances, all their time—and their energy to the work of an Irish National Theatre. They were earnest, intense, and devoted men, following the artistic leadership of Yeats and Lady Gregory, who, incidentally, demanded servility of all her acquaintances. Neither Joyce nor I had pliant knees, and so we kept each other company.

It was Lady Gregory who decided that Yeats's friends were to present him on his fortieth birthday with a copy of the rare Kelmscott Chaucer, which had been printed at Kelmscott by that fount of energy, William Morris, a friend of both Yeats and his father. At the time, I had not seen Yeats for three years—through no neglect of mine, but due rather to his residing in London. I used to see him when he stayed at the Cavendish Hotel, which was within half a dozen doors of my home in Rutland Square. I recall that Joyce and I were passing the place in a tram one evening, and I pointed it out to him, mentioning the Chaucer birthday presentation. Without a word, Joyce left the tram. In those days you were not obliged to wait for a tram or bus stop. I saw him hurry to the hotel and disappear inside. Afterwards, Joyce told me that Yeats himself had opened the door of his apartment, and that without prefacing his remark he had bluntly asked Yeats how old he was.

"What did he say?" I asked.

"He told me that he was forty."

Silence. . . . You had to prod Joyce for information, for he rarely volunteered anything.

"And what did you say?" I persisted.

"I said, 'I am sorry. You are too old for me to help. Good-by.' "

Jealousy or resentment of the Lady Gregory "outfit" may have prompted Joyce's behavior, although he was defying nearly everything at the time. It was strange, however, how Yeats could be impressed by such brazen rudeness. Perhaps audacity attracted him. In any event, he had an astonishing faculty for being able to disassociate a person from his actions. Yeats never allowed his critical judgment to be swayed by his personal likes or dislikes. For instance, many years after the birthday misadven-

ture, Yeats told me that since he had read Joyce's *Ulysses,*
every other kind of writing seemed insipid.

Joyce and I were walking down Sackville Street past
Byrne's, the stationer's, when he told me of the foregoing
incident. He announced it with an air of challenge, but
I made no comment. Inwardly I was shocked. I have respect for gifted men, and I could not see how Joyce could
help Yeats. Without warning, Joyce turned abruptly into
the shop, which sold a few cheap books in addition to
newspapers and stationery. As I glanced in the window
my eye caught a little paper-bound book, *Lays of the
Moy* by Gerald Griffin, a young namesake of the better-
known poet. The little volume had caught Joyce's eye,
too, for when asked why he had rushed into the shop, he
answered with almost a sigh of relief, "I was seeing if
they were better poems than mine!" Perhaps jealousy was
the explanation for Joyce's rudeness to Yeats. It was
never directly manifested except on rare and trivial occasions such as this, but I suspect that it was there all the
time.

Apart from the farcical situations which arose from
time to time, it has always been my impression that Yeats's
association with the occult retarded the acceptance of the
dramatic movement in Ireland. His dabbling in astrology,
magic, seances, mysticism, and the occult in general, however, was secondary to the devotion of his life—Poetry. In
other words, Yeats dealt in mysticism merely to enrich the
subconscious, from which all inspiration flows. With AE
it was otherwise. Russell preferred philosophy to poetry,

even though for him philosophy was largely theosophy. An acquaintance of mine, whose parents were Irish and Spanish, complained that all Irish poetry was "anent"; that is, it referred to something other than it said. This was particularly true of AE's poetry. "Anentness" made the populace suspicious, and especially so since they felt that the Abbey Theatre had little use for Roman Catholics. It remained for Yeats to overcome this unpopularity, but it took twenty years to make the grudging admit that his patriotism was pure, selfless, and ideal.

On the other hand, I have never looked lightly upon Yeats's tampering with the spirit world—not since the time he entered a room in my house in Ely Place, Dublin, stood in the doorway, and said, "There is a presence here, I smell incense." Yeats had had no way of knowing that my wife and I had just been talking about a friend— a priest—lately dead. Yeats used to say that to talk about a dead person is to bring their ghost about you. Since then I have never scoffed at ghosts.

Yeats loved to detect in simple people simple beliefs. He once told me of an incident that took place when he was traveling by train to Galway. Yeats had just been elected Senator of the Irish Free State. A countryman, finding a door in the corridor locked, turned to him and said as though all things were possible to a man in an exalted position, "Will you open it, Senator?" There was a hint of amiable malice like that of a leprechaun in Yeats's appreciation of humorous adventures of this sort, and from them he derived an enjoyment out of proportion to their significance. For instance, Yeats once remarked to Lady Gregory, "I hear that the Sister Superior of the school where Gogarty's daughter is said to her: 'There are five bad men who are destroying Dublin: Russell, Yeats, Liam O'Flaherty, Lennox Robinson, and—' she stopped." Evidently, the fifth man was Gogarty, and the idea amused Yeats no end.

Yeats hated hatred. This probably explains why one so word-compelling had few terms of invective or of scorn. His nature was too deep for hatred. His only retaliation against George Moore's attacks on him was to attempt to pillory Moore in the dialogue of some play. Moore had at one time likened Yeats to "an umbrella forgotten at a picnic." Yeats retorted that Moore looked like "a face carved out of a turnip."

On one occasion, however, repartee failed Yeats altogether. He had applied for permission to read in the great library of Trinity College. Every applicant must take an oath in Latin swearing not to damage books. Yeats must have applied to Mahaffy, because it was Mahaffy who sent him a copy of the oath, with the quantities marked for pronunciation by Mahaffy himself, and the message, "For I have a sensitive ear." I offered to write a sardonic reply to Mahaffy, but Yeats would have none of it. For all I know, he took Mahaffy's insolence lying down.

And yet Yeats had wit enough to defend himself. On one of his three visits to the United States, which he grew to like the more he knew of the country and its people, he was reading his poetry to an audience in Pittsburgh when a woman who turned out to be a teacher of elocution challenged his method.

"Will you kindly tell me, Mr. Yeats, why you read your poetry in that manner?"

"I read my poetry as all the great poets from Homer down have read their poetry."

But she was not satisfied.

"Will Mr. Yeats give me his authority for saying that Homer read his poetry in that manner?"

Unhesitatingly he answered, "The only authority I can give is the authority a Scotchman gave when he claimed Shakespeare for his own country, 'The ability of the man justifies the assumption.'"

Yeats always regarded England as a foreign country though he resided there frequently and had many friends there. As an Irish poet, in him all the traditions and sentiments of Ireland met. He was impatient of England, a country so largely composed of bourgeois. To him the bourgeois mind was a "middle-class" mind. His cry was for a return to the simple folk, to the heroic folk. When Yeats heard that in Russia Lenin had declared religion to be the "opium of the masses," Yeats remarked, "In England H. G. Wells is the opium of the middle classes."

Yeats was susceptible to beauty to the end of his days. Some shrewd journalist in San Francisco was the first to notice that interviews by male reporters only bored Yeats. From this he deduced Yeats's preference for female society. This is far too dogmatic. That Yeats admired American women for their *chic* and for their intelligence was undoubted. He had compared them to English women, to the disadvantage of the latter. And this remark, made somewhere in New York, was very badly received in London. But Yeats could take his place among men and was often the most forceful of them all when it came to dispute. J. M. Hone, in his life of Yeats (Macmillan, 1943), states, and is not out of place here:

> He had the powerful lower lip which reveals the born orator and the born pugilist; a certain disdain, a certain pugnacity is necessary both to the pugilist and to the orator. In addressing large audiences he was sometimes uneasy at the start, and would then stride up and down the platform in a rather surprising manner before he attained his natural distinction of bearing, his gravity of utterance, and his rhythm. His voice was musical, touched with melancholy, the tones rising and falling in a continuous flow of sound. He lingered on certain words as if to avoid a hiatus, as it were, but the pauses when they occurred were timed and still full of sound, like the musical pauses in the execution of a master. This cadenced utterance was most characteristic . . .

Being as he was the most rhythmical of verse-makers, naturally he loved the sound of words. I recall an incident which may seem to be somewhat facetious, but it is such a good illustration of what I mean, and it is so characteristic of Yeats that I may be forgiven for repeating it.

In his old age, he was accustomed to go abroad to sunnier climes to escape the Dublin winters (to say nothing of Dublin summers). One year, when he was wintering at Majorca, he was attended by a Spanish doctor who had written a letter to Yeats's Irish doctor. Wishing an interpretation in the words of a layman, Yeats showed me the letter. I read a quaint sentence to this effect:

"We have here an antique cardio-sclerotic of advanced years." Not wishing to impart the gravity of such a message, I said that it was doctor's Greek to me, and that it would be all Greek to him. He insisted, however, and so I read rather slurringly, for the letter boded little health. "Read it slowly and distinctly," he ordered. There was no escape, and so I read it slowly and distinctly. He inclined his head. "Read that again." He followed the cadence with his finger. At last as the sound died away, he exclaimed, utterly ignoring the meaning:

"Do you know that I would rather be called 'Cardio-Sclerotic' than 'Lord of Lower Egypt'?"

How, it may be asked, can a poet have a musical ear and yet be, as Yeats was, completely tone deaf? Many tales are told of Yeats's tone deafness. In spite of his early experiments with a psaltry to wed words to music and of the co-operation of Dolmnetsch the musical instrument-maker and of the actress, Florence Farr, Yeats was bored by music, which he did not trouble to understand, and he was bored worse by the extenuation of words for the sake of the music. Compton Mackenzie, the Scotch novelist and patriot, told me that when he had attended a concert in Dublin with Yeats (it was on some official occasion, the Tailteann Games, I think), they had entered the box just as John McCormack was singing Yeats's "Down by the Salley Gardens." Mackenzie drew Yeats's attention to the song. Yeats listened for a moment and then when he had at last caught a word or two, remarked, "Oh, the deadly audibility of the fellow." And Lady Gregory records that when the pianist Rummell gave a recital at the Abbey auditorium for the actors, who for reasons of safety could not leave the theatre between matinee and evening, Yeats fell asleep during the playing of Beethoven's "Moonlight Sonata," and upon awakening said that he had dreamed that there was a storm going on.

In his middle age Yeats's health improved. He could swim with me in the half-frozen deep water of Dublin Bay at Sandycove. At this time, he affected to have a bad memory. Indeed, he added this to his fund of "withdrawals" to avoid bores or to escape tedious conversation.

One day I had occasion to remark in his hearing that Aeschylus called Memory the "Mother of the Muses." From that day on Yeats never forgot a thing.

Yeats could be simple as a child and childlike when some new thought struck him. To those who did not understand him, or who were jealous of him, his unconscious attitudinizing appeared to be a deliberate pose. Sir William Watson was one who made this great mistake. Here is what he wrote, and I know he meant Yeats, for I knew Watson well:

> I met a poet lately, one of those
> To whom his life was one continual pose.
> A wise man this, for, take the pose away,
> What else were left 'twould pose the gods to say.

I never told Yeats of Watson's lines. Perhaps if I had, he would have given us an epigram such as the one he gave AE when AE asked him to praise a poet whom Yeats regarded as an imitator:

> You say, as I have often given tongue
> In praise of what another's said or sung,
> 'Twere politic to do the like by these;
> But was there ever dog that praised his fleas?

I have written so much about Yeats's foibles that it is time I tried to describe him in the vein that has made him the chief poet of our time.

Yeats composed with what appeared to be great mental agony. With his hands behind his back, his head down, or suddenly looking up, he would pace the floor, humming and murmuring to himself until the poem arose from the rich darkness within him. I observed him at work at my house when he was composing "What Finger First Began," one of the songs in a late play of his. It was suggested by a Chinese legend that those who hear aerial music are listening to the music of a lost kingdom.

It took him several minutes of humming to get the second line.

> What finger first began
> Music of a lost kingdom?

As the rhythm-wedded words came, he wrote them in pencil on odd pieces of paper. I found many such pieces of paper in my study when he had finished his poem.

When Yeats read poetry, it mattered not whose it was, he always got the pitch of the verse, as it were, by murmuring to himself with an intensity of interest that he always exhibited for poetry. He was most generous, always interested in other people's work, and did not appear to realize what a favor he was conferring by altering or correcting entire lines. When I wrote *A Serious Thing*, during the Black and Tan atrocities, for the Abbey Theatre, Yeats told me that if I left out the psychoanalysis of Pilate's wife who "had a dream," it would be one of the most powerful political plays ever written, for I had compared the resurrection of Lazarus in answer to a divine call to the *risorgimento* of Ireland. The Black and Tans in the audience were too stupid to see the irony—they applauded the piece. I could not leave out the analysis of Pilate's wife, however, because I believed that this new sophistry would wreak havoc upon untrained minds, and I wanted to kill it by ridicule in its cradle. I did not succeed, and spoiled instead what could have been pruned into a good play had I listened to the Master.

When he was reading my book of verse before recommending it to his sisters' press, the Cuala, Yeats would offer suggestions that I invariably accepted gratefully. "Intensity" of phrase was one of his aims, the pouncing and surprising word. I have a list somewhere of the alterations that Yeats made in pencil and which I adopted in my book. It is not of sufficient interest to recall them now, but I remember that almost an entire stanza of "Palinode" was written by Yeats. He was generous in all things but in this especially.

There are few things in this life which give as much satisfaction as the friendship of good and famous men. To have known someone as strange as Yeats is, like Poetry, "its own exceeding great reward." There was an aura about the man that was almost palpable. You could feel his presence in the dark even if you had not met him for a year. It was as though he had more spirit than his body could contain, and it stood about him like the aura round the moon. There was inspiration in his presence. From Augustus John's lips I borrow a sentence that he applied to Lady Gregory's nephew. It is more appropriate to Yeats, "He was one of those rare ones who, single-handed, is able to enrich and dignify an entire nation." I would add, "And to redeem it."

My Friend Flaherty

How DO I JUDGE A MAN? BY
the way I feel when I am leaving him. Do I come away
feeling like a roebuck with antlers high, a "stag of ten";
or do I feel as if I had given him a pint of my blood?

There are some men who send a gloom after you that
lowers your resistance till a little thing like a ragweed
can knock you out after only a short session with your
jinx, and you have to submit yourself to a bartender for
a course of psychological rehabilitation. Such men are
unlucky. They cannot help it; but they'll get you—for
there is ill will somewhere. And, no matter how free you
are from superstition, you cannot ward it off.

But there are other men, big men, like the sun on the
sea; and there are merry little men with dancing eyes,
with a laugh in their speech and an advancing hand, who
tell tales full of adventure with nothing sinister or tragic
in them. For men meet with those adventures only to which
their character is attuned. And when you leave one of
those fellows, you feel as if a crowd were cheering you or
as if you had just been saluted by a sergeant of police.

My Friend Flaherty

The man I am writing about does me good to meet. It would do you good, too, merely to see him: a big, expansive man with a face florid with enthusiasm and eyes clear as the Northern Ice, which he spent so much of his time exploring when he created one of his most famous pictures, *Nanook of the North.* I often regret that I never met Walt Whitman. But there is a lot of him reincarnated in Bob Flaherty, who is further removed from the mediocre than any man I've ever known. For he, too, can take you into space—"to behold the birth of stars, to learn one of the meanings, to launch off with absolute faith and never be quiet again." And the more faith we have the easier will it be for us, when our time comes, to glide down the slips.

But absolute faith in what, you may ask? Absolute faith in the nature and the fate of man, a belief that there is a hero hidden in all men, and that when we are all in the same boat the hero will steer it. This is somewhat vague and abstract; but so is faith.

Bob Flaherty feels the need of great scenes where man is elemental, and unspoiled by sophistication and machinery. This need can be felt in his picture, *Man of Aran.* It is what brought him to the extreme edge of Europe, to the last bulwark of the land where the limestone cliffs stand up three hundred feet and shoulder off seas that break in spray fifty feet above them, waves that come unimpeded all the way from Brazil. Here he found his Man of Aran, Tiger King, tugging at his oar with innate skill a few points off the direct onset of the crashing seas. Here he composed his fabulous odyssey of a gaunt and treeless Atlantic island where man fights for bare existence against wind and rain and sea.

He loves to tell how Tiger King visited the United States and the journalists gathered to meet him on the ship and sailed up the Hudson with him. When they were passing the Empire State Building, one of them pointed to it and asked, "What do you think of that?" Tiger King pointed still higher to where the sun was breaking through a cloud and replied, "What do *you* think of *that?*" Then comes a characteristic anecdote about Bernard Shaw. When Epstein was doing a bust of the great man he brought Tiger King to the studio, thinking that he would keep Shaw quiet. When they left Shaw was telling King how a curragh should be steered in rough seas!

There is an island in Hudson Bay, about seventy miles long, called Flaherty's Island, for it was he who found it. "How big is it?" I asked when I first heard of it. "It has two horizons," was his answer, a good one, for there are wide horizons in the man himself. He is the dramatic poet of the screen, the only one who has realized to what heights of art it could be exalted and made to outdo the drama of the stage.

While creating *Nanook of the North* he heard of an old Eskimo and his wife who were attacked by a starving bear. The Eskimos, it seems, always keep a little lamp of seal oil burning in their igloos, which the women alone can attend. Attracted by the smell of this, which is about one of the most penetrating smells in the world, the white bear climbed on the roof of the igloo, where the ice is very thin. The old woman woke up to see a long neck and black snout swinging from side to side in its search for a way in. She nudged her husband who awoke, took his spear, and crept out into the Arctic darkness. He had only one chance, and on that the lives of his wife and himself depended: he had to hit the bear behind the left shoulder and kill him at once. He cast his spear in the dim light, slew the bear, and crept back into his igloo and fell asleep. For him it was only an incident in the daily routine.

Flaherty says a young Eskimo can spear and land a walrus weighing 2,000 pounds. "Are they strong?" I asked. "If you took an Eskimo and set him down with a pick and shovel in a hole in a New York street, he would be useless. If you set a New York laborer down on the Greenlandic ice sheet he would perish in two days!" And listen to this, for Flaherty is a phrase-maker, and his generalities reveal deep thinking: "Every man is strong enough for the work on which his life depends."

In his great dramas of the lives of elemental people he has the Shakespearian power of remaining off stage, unseen and unsuspected, so thoroughly does he project his creations. This was borne in on me when a friend asked, "But what would the film be but for Nanook?" Like Tiger King, I pointed higher. "And what would Nanook be but for Flaherty?"

When Flaherty tells a story his face is transfigured. It becomes lit with the light of the visionary scene. You can see the glare from the snow when he tells of an impatient and unpopular missionary who got snow blindness, fell into a crevasse, and became gangrenous from the waist down. During weeks of agony, while the dead flesh was being whittled away with a stone knife by an Eskimo woman, the missionary kept raving all the time about his approaching marriage.

The world is Flaherty's stage. From the Pole to the tropical Isthmus of Panama he can range and can tell of the trade that Spain did with China at the time of the conquistadors. All the precious art of the Chinese Empire —lacquer, silk, jade, and porcelain—had to be taken across the Isthmus by portage. Many priceless treasures were seized by bandits and recovered from their descendants by a dealer just recently. It was there a Chinese princess, on her way to visit the court of Spain, was captured and sold to a tribe of native Indians who to this day revere her as a saint: the Virgin of Guadalupe.

But it is not Flaherty's storytelling that makes him the most magnanimous man I've met. It is his power of making you forget the trivial things in life and look only at the elemental things that build up the dignity of man. "If only men were honest, there would be no wars." His face glows with the wonder of a child when he tells of the hidden paradises on the earth; or when he meets a friend. His finger never mutes the strings that vibrate in eternity. He has in him the expansiveness and generosity of the true American.

There is no limit to the length of time you can put in at his farm, which lies halfway up a wooded mountain in Vermont; a real farm that produces food and life. Thinking of this generosity of his, I dimly recalled the fact that to be princely, in Gaelic, meant to be like the

O'Flaherty when the head of the clan ruled West Connaught. And there is a word very like the name "Flaherty" which means to be overgenerous, to have illimitable liberality. I recently met Dr. Hurley, the Gaelic scholar, and I asked him if I were right. This is what he wrote out for me: *O'Flaith*bearthy (O'Flaherty) *Flaithe*amail, Flaith (Floh)—a prince. I knew that there was something appropriate in that princely name of his.

To the regions where his mind dwells few of us can commute, so the best we can do is to take care that we do not miss him when he comes to town. I hear that he is to be at the Coffee House Club for lunch today. Where is my hat?

Museum Piece

George, OR, AS HIS NAME WAS
originally, Georges, could talk French like a linguaphone.
His mother was French, and although she had been for
years in the United States before George was born, she
had not forgotten her little home-town five hundred miles
south of Paris. It was for her a bit of Paris, hidden high
in the Pyrenees, more than two thousand feet above the
level of the sea, a tiny town, hardly an acre in extent. But
though it was small, it boasted thirty hotels and pensions
built on its two streets, which were separated by an inter-
vening park. So narrow was the gorge of Eaux Bonnes
in which the town was built that the cliffs had to be blasted
to make room for the houses, the back rooms of which were
laid against the living rock.

George and I were at a replacement camp when we got
leave. Patton's boys were taking a well-earned rest. Though
a replacement camp may be rest, it is not leave. But there
the doctor's word is law: two weeks' leave for George to
cure his battle fatigue. George decided to go to Eaux
Bonnes. He went so that he could bring news of it to his

mother when at last we should be at a separation station far from the scenes of slaughter and the crash of shells. He could hardly hope to find any of his kin alive there, for it was more than fifty years since his mother left Eaux Bonnes. Yet it was worth a visit. Well worth one as it proved to be for George.

He had not gone six days when a telegram came to me:

AM IN ROMANTIC SPOT. NEED HELP. COME RIGHT AWAY.

GEORGE.

It was just like George to leave me guessing. What did "romantic spot" mean? I knew quite well that, with its château, its cascades and its shady walks through the pine forests that surrounded it, Eaux Bonnes was a romantic spot. It would be more like George to get himself in a "spot" through what is vulgarly known as "romance" when love is meant. Yes, that would be more like George's form. For that then my help was needed. George had left Paris all alone, so any trouble he was in must have arisen through his meeting with someone in Eaux Bonnes. It was not my business to reason why when George was in a spot. Off I went. To reach my destination, I had to travel two days, and to overcome many war-time obstacles, which have no place in this true tale.

He was staying in the Hôtel d'If, the last one in the street to the right of the little park beside the Museum which once must have been the town gaol. George was sitting outside his hotel. When the diligence in which I was riding rattled along the pave, George shouted, "Hi!" The *cocher* reined in and George lifted out my bag.

"Before I tell you a thing, you must have a drink," George announced.

He was in such high spirits that I began to wonder how he could be in any trouble and if my long trek had not been in vain. His eyes were blinking bright: gone was all trace of his battle fatigue.

To the boy who came for my luggage George said, "Room number three." Then to me he explained that he had made all arrangements and had gotten the only front room that was available. "The back rooms in this town are useful only for coiling wall paper." Then he shouted, "Emil," and Monsieur Thiange, the proprietor, appeared. He was plump, rosy, and good-natured. He bowed when he was introduced to me.

"Here's the man that got me out of the spot. And didn't he do it well?" M. Thiange smiled. He did not understand English, but he knew what we were talking about from George's exuberance. He smiled. George slapped him on the back and thanked him again in his native dialect.

If M. Thiange could not speak English, he could be eloquent in cuisine. The lunch with its choice wine, was just right for a travel-wearied man. I only toyed with the perfect omelette. I was too tired to eat, so I will say, "when I had drunk the most palatable lunch" I had had in many a long day, George led me outside to the right along the road that is closed by the majestic Pic de Ger crowned by eternal snow.

"Stop laughing, George," I said. "What does this mean?" I produced his telegram and pointed to the first four words.

He slapped me on the shoulder and said, still smiling, "I will tell you."

This is the story that George unfolded to me.

"It all began with one of those vinaigrettes, those little donkey-carriages like that one over there. These little vehicles are often hired by people to attend them in their walks and take them up the steeper paths, for this place fills up with old people in the season. Shortly after I came here, I thought that I would walk through the woods and come out near the spur on which the château stands and find out if visitors were allowed to see the old place. I was just coming out after about an hour's walk and climb on one of the little tracks that lead up to it when, to my astonishment, I heard a girl's voice calling to me. She said that if I left the wood and came out on the path, I could help her. I need not say that I lost no time. I vaulted over the wall that bounded the path on the forest side. On the other side there was a bit of a drop of about fifty feet. An old gentleman with a white moustache sat in a vinaigrette, but the donkey refused to budge an inch farther, and the thing could not be turned.

" 'It is my father,' she said. 'I must get him home before nightfall. This place gets very cold after sundown and I am afraid to let him climb so far. His heart is none too strong.' I told her my name and rank and saluted the old gentleman. 'Where does he live?' I asked. She raised her arm and pointed to the château.

"Well, the first thing to do was to examine the donkey. The donkeys here are very small, smaller than the ponies they have in Norway for pulling contraptions like this.

'He might as well be a mule, he is so obstinate,' the old man volunteered, who was evidently angry or hungry. Anyway, he did not relish being made to look like a fool sitting behind a donkey that would not budge.

"I went over the donkey's hooves; and, sure enough, what did I find but a piece of glass sticking in the quick of his left fore hoof. There was blood on it and all round the shoe. With my knife I got it out at last. It took me half an hour, for I was afraid that I would break the glass and leave a piece in. But I got it all out apparently, for the vinaigrette began to move.

"Soon we came out of the woods and on to a real road that wound up to the château. The queerest servants you ever saw were rushing about and thinking they were helping the old man, who got out under his own power and stood by my side. I realized that he was ushering me in to his house with the formal politeness of a French nobleman. He was the Comte Gaston du Bar. His people had lived here ever since they had come out of the mists of the north to conquer the aborigines centuries ago. There was not a bath in the room to which I was sent for a wash-up; but an old bearded fellow and a maid carried in a tin tub of tepid water and a few brass ewers full of boiling water, soap and towels; and they set the tub and a brush and comb on the floor. Well, I washed up and then a bugle blew and the old fellow with the beard came back and told me that he would conduct me to the drawing room. The Comte and his daughter were standing before a log fire, for, as the girl had said, it got cold up at the elevation, and in that stone fortress of a house it certainly was cold.

When I entered, the old man smiled and said, 'My daughter and I were just remarking on the excellent French you speak. I thought that I detected the accent of the neighborhood. Were you born in this region?' 'No,' I said, 'I was born in America and I learned any French I know over there.' I did not let him know that my mother was a native of Eaux Bonnes which turned out to be all for the best as you shall see. I had not much time to tell him even if I had intended, for just at the moment another servant came in to announce that dinner was served. He asked me how much furlough I had. I told him that I had fourteen days, two of which were gone, and that it would take me two days to travel back to camp. He asked how it was possible to leave when an army was in action. I explained that I was sent to a replacement center and that the doctor ordered me off for the good of my health. So I chose this quiet neighborhood, with its lovely scenery, water springs and piny air. He seemed to unbend a little at that.

"In spite of the formality, his daughter did not ask me to give her my arm. I did not offer it, but followed on while the Comte brought up the rear.

"I will skip the dinner. I was asked as many questions as a captured paratrooper. Then it was my turn. I asked enough to learn that before the war they had an automobile for moving about but, now that they could get no *essence*, it was laid up. Mam'selle rode into the village every other day. I made a note of that and hoped that tomorrow would be one of those other days. It was.

"You can't go through Eaux Bonnes without being seen by half the inhabitants. And a young lady unchaperoned cannot visit a male friend in a pension or hotel. I saw her on horseback with a long green velvet-looking riding habit cantering into the town on a badly groomed chestnut mare. I did not like to claim acquaintance, for every one was staring, so I thought of a simple plan. Why not go back up through the woods to where she would have to walk her horse and then come out and have a pleasant *tête-à-tête?* I did; and it was a great success. The 'other day' telescoped into every day, until one morning, I got another invitation to dine at the château. Perhaps I should have been delighted but, knowing the old man, I was filled with misgivings, especially when I realized that our meetings might have very well been observed from the château that stood like a sentry on the hill.

"My misgivings were justified. After dinner the old man asked his daughter to excuse us. We were going to the library.

"He took me into a large room smelling of musty leather. There was leather everywhere, leather gilded, leather tooled, and leather plain. Every book was bound, and the bigger ones were embossed with the coat of arms of the house. There were coats of arms everywhere, even on the window in stained glass.

"He put me into a chair but did not sit down himself. He began:

" 'For the last four days you have been meeting my daughter without my permission. She is a very lonely, and therefore a susceptible young lady, and in the upset and turbulent state of my country, it might well be expected that she should seek an alliance with somebody who would appeal to her by attributes of the strange and remote, which are the attributes of romance, and these you happen at the moment to possess. My daughter needs not to look beyond France for a *parti*. That had been arranged for her before her mother's death. I have no way of knowing your *bona fides*. You may have sufficient means in your own country to support my daughter; but nothing could give her more, or as much, as she already has. No French woman can be happy outside France. Much less in a country where the very architecture is alien to us.'

"I was about to tell him about my mother but he gave me no opening. He went on, 'Therefore I must ask you not to meet my daughter in public again. Hers is not a name to be bandied about by the gossip of a countryside. When in France, you must conform to the rules. Never again. . . .'

"At that I very nearly lost my temper. I was about to tell him that it was about time they changed the rules in France, seeing to what a mess they had brought his country, when in came Mademoiselle du Bar.

"She was on the verge of tears. With shining eyes she turned on her father:

" 'This is a nice way to treat a guest, a man who saved you from pneumonia. I know that you have been warning him off me. I know that you said America is full of wooden houses, and no place for a French woman. I tell you that I don't care. He is not a GI flirting with a foreign woman whom he will forget as soon as he gets home. . . . He is a plain-speaking, straightforward and dependable American. . . . You have only got to look at his face and think of what he and his comrades have done for France.' Then came the tears.

"And then I got the fright of my life. When I turned to face the old gentleman, his face was not only purple but the strangest kind of red I ever saw on a human face or any other face, painted or natural. He stood quite still and that face of his blazed and shone like a neon light. His daughter either did not see it, or she did not mind. But I did and I thought that I saw a demon or some avenging angel with face aflame. Then he moved; and all of a sudden I saw that it was the sinking sun on the heraldic window throwing its colors on the face of the man to whom they belonged. Gules was the color, and its name comes from 'gula,' the gullet of a wild beast. That is one thing we don't have in the U. S. A. Old men with faces gules.

"Next morning I was awakened out of a light sleep by a scratching noise at my door. A piece of paper was being forced under it. I waited until it was fully in. Then I opened the door to see who was outside, but I am at a corner beside the passage to the back of the house, so I saw no one when I looked out. I opened the note. It read: Meet me in the museum, 5:00 P.M. Ermengarde.

"The note paper was like old ivory. There was a coat of arms at the top. There was no doubt about its authenticity. Even without the blazon, the handwriting alone could be only Ermengarde's. Who could have brought it? What did that matter beside the chance of seeing her? My only regret was that I had been wakened too early. The day would be long to pass till five.

"The museum was an ancient building with high walls, lighted from a glass dome in the roof, and it looked like an armory or a gaol. At the back was a little garden bounded by the sheer cliff and by walls as high as the museum. What a junk shop it was! I never saw a more disorderly joint in my life. It might have been a scrap house for the overflows of the attics of the château. The sword of Gaston Phoebus; the armorial andirons from the Château de Couterets; an engraved stone from the old Roman Building now called the Maison Carrèe; tapestries from unused bedrooms of the Château du Bar; helmets and halberds and a stuffed trout from the Lac de Gaube; vases and candelabra everywhere, so that we could not walk abreast. But it was not to see antiques that we had come.

"We took refuge in the little garden at the back. It had a table and a few chairs and it was cool with water trickling down the rock.

"Ermengarde seemed to be embarrassed when she looked at the empty chairs and realized that we were the only visitors. To cheer her I said that she must have been very brave to defy her father. She brightened at that and said with a quiet little smile, 'We are not meeting *in public.*'

"She is beautiful and gentle. I hope that when you come to marry, you will have the good luck to meet someone like her.

"We talked on and on. We could have talked till daybreak, but she had to get back in time for dinner. In the valley it was already getting dark.

"At last we rose to go, when to our amazement we found that we had been locked in. The curator had turned the key and locked the old junk-shop and us in it. In the darkness I was afraid to move for fear of losing my way and being separated. I could not reach any of the windows of this ancient gaol. I whistled and yelled and banged on the door with an old brass candlestick. But it was no use. The door was thick enough to defy a battering ram. I had neither match nor lighter. Ermengarde seemed to me to be weeping. I felt her trembling as if with sobs.

" 'I'll tell you what we'll do,' I said. 'You stay here at the door and I'll go and bring those chairs in from the garden, and we shall have something on which to sit. It looks as if we are locked up for the night. I'll drag the chairs in one by one. Call to me when you hear me coming back.'

" 'You are not going to leave me?' she cried. And I knew that she was weeping, though I could not see her face.

" 'All right. We'll go together. We at least can play hide and seek.' She was in no mood to follow my humour. She caught my sleeve.

" 'Do not let us part.'

" 'If I could find one of the andirons that caught my eye as I came in, I might be able to take it apart and to throw a bit of it out of the window. That might attract attention.'

"She fell upon her knees and cried silently. Then she sobbed,

" 'I am disgraced and my family with me. This will break my father's heart. I had rather that the place went on fire.'

" 'Leave him to me,' I said reassuringly.

" 'But . . . but what can you do? What can anyone do? We can't get out.'

" 'I will tell him exactly what happened and ask him if he distrusts his own flesh and blood. I will tell him that if he takes the trouble to learn anything about America, he will find that the women there are as independent as the men, and more so. And that to stay out half the night, or the whole night, if it comes to that, need not necessarily mean a thing.'

" 'Is that true?'

" 'I'm darned well sure it is. And, furthermore, I will ask him to come to the States if he doesn't believe me. If he won't do that, I'll have my mother over here to meet him. She'll tell him where he gets off. So comfort your dear heart.' For a long time she was silent. I hoped that she was taking in what I had said. She must have risen from her knees, for the sighs were as high as my chin.

"I said, 'If I could get something for us to sit on, a tapestry or a cushion; but I am afraid that the silly exhibits will come down on our heads if I pull at anything. Put your back to the door and sit on my coat.'

" 'I can wind my skirt round and sit on that. Do you think that they will open the place early?'

"There I was on a spot. I had forgotten on what days the infernal place was open. I had even forgotten what

day of the week it was, Friday or Saturday. If it was
Saturday and the place was kept shut till Monday, it
would be just too bad.

"I need not tell you what a miserable night we put in.
I never felt so tired. All the good my leave did me slipped
away and I could hardly think. At last sleep came and
when I wakened, some light was coming through the dome.
I looked and saw her asleep by my side with one raised
arm above her head. I waited half an hour, fearing to
awaken her until I could hear the sound of a passerby or
the noise of the town. Then I could get something with
which either to break the lock or throw through the window to attract attention. At last I heard the sound of a
cart. I woke her in order that the banging I intended to
make against the door would not startle her out of sleep.
And didn't I whack that door. Until it sounded like the
biggest drum that ever was made. The cart stopped. Then
it moved on. I smothered my disappointment by telling
her that very soon the town would be astir.

"Imagine my delight when I heard a key rasping the
lock. And who do you think appeared? M. Thiange!
He was the curator. It was he who had locked us in.

" 'I am devastated,' he cried. 'I saw no one when I
closed this place last night. Can I ever be forgiven? Thank
God the hue and cry is over now. Mam'selle is found. The
Comte will be overjoyed. He thought that she had flown
away.'

" 'What's all this about a hue and cry?' I asked.

" 'Messengers came from the castle to ask if you were

with me at the hotel. I sought you, but you had not slept in your room. They feared the worst. But now! What transports of joy await M. le Comte!'

" 'Let me out of this. I must see my father without delay. I must go home,' Ermengarde cried. She looked so haughty and sweet I could have kissed her, there and then.

" 'I can't let you get the works all alone. I will go with you,' I said.

" 'No, No!' she replied. 'I will take M. Thiange, the curator. He owes it to me to explain how it came about that he locked us in. If you come, it will make things worse for me.'

"Thiange bowed and smiled. 'That will be an honor. I myself will explain and make my apologies to the Comte. Indeed yes, yes.'

"It was a deadly long wait as it seemed to me before Thiange returned. During that time I wired for you, for I wanted you to testify to my good character for one thing, and to assure the old Comte that I was all right so far as finances went at home. There was no one in France I could think of but you, and I knew that you would not fail me.

"At last M. Thiange returned. He was jubilant. He kissed me on both cheeks and congratulated me vehemently.

" 'What the . . . ?' I asked.

" 'Felicitations! The Comte has consented to the match?'

" 'What match?'

" 'You may marry his daughter and he will give you both his blessing.'

" 'What is this? What did he say?'

" 'He asked me if it were true that it was accidently that you were locked up in the museum. I assured him on that point. He said that, nevertheless, he would send for the curator. I bowed.

" 'I am the curator.'

" 'I confessed that I had locked up the museum a little early because it seemed quite empty when I looked in. You must have been in the garden at the back. He asked me to describe the museum. I told him that it was a strong building, as became a place so full of precious objects, the sword of Gaston Phoebus (one of his forebears by the way), armor, tapestries, and furniture. I handed him the catalogue.

" 'When he came to the bed in which Queen Victoria had slept, a change overcame him. That bed which had for so long failed to impress our visitors, had a surprising influence on the Comte. It cast a quiet spell upon him. His vehemence died away. He grew silent and pensive. M. le Comte was a changed man. He turned and embraced his daughter and said that she might marry the man of her heart.

" 'Now, I bring you his message. It is to be kept profoundly secret between us.'

" 'The bed in which Queen Victoria slept? Is there such a bed? I did not see it,' I exclaimed. Thiange answered, 'It is a four-poster bed. It used to stand in the middle of the museum, but the decorum of the thing was lost on our public; besides, it took up too much space so I had it dismantled and the ends are used now to shut off the fireplace, which can be very drafty when the wind is southwest. You can read about it in the folder I showed the Comte.' He handed me a crumpled Guide to Eaux Bonnes. I read, 'Visitors should not omit a visit to the town museum. It contains many objects of great interest, sentiment and antiquity, among them a bed in which Queen Victoria is known to have slept *circa* 1863.' "

DANS CE LIT A DORMI LA REINE VICTORIA

At this point I interrupted, for I could not help myself. I am afraid that I laughed out loud,

"What a break," I exclaimed.

"You said it," said George. "It was a break. But, you see, Thiange is my uncle."